ROOSTERS CAN CAUSE CONCUSSIONS

And Other Things They Didn't Teach Me in Medical School

BRIAN BENFIELD, MD

HIDDEN FIELDS PRESS

Roosters Can Cause Concussions: And Other Things They Didn't Teach Me in Medical School

ISBN: 979-8-9879768-4-5

First Edition
Published in the United States by Hidden Fields Press.

For more information or to contact the author visit brianbenfieldmd.com.

The stories in this book are written for entertainment purposes, only. The names of patients and other individuals have been changed to respect their privacy.

No material included is intended to be a substitute for professional medical advice, diagnosis, or treatment. Always seek the advice of your physician or other qualified health care provider with any questions you may have regarding a medical condition or treatment and before undertaking a new health care regimen. Never disregard professional medical advice or delay in seeking it because of something you have read in this book.

To my wonderful wife, Ellen.
The best part of my day has always been coming home
and sharing my stories with you.
Seeing your face light up and hearing you laugh
meant the story was book-worthy.

CONTENTS

THE INSPIRATION FOR A BOOK

It was the winter of 2000 and the Shelby Children's Clinic was right in the middle of a horrible flu epidemic. I had finished my pediatric residency only a few months earlier and was overwhelmed by the sheer volume of patients we were seeing each day. My nurse told me I had one more patient to see, but truthfully, I was just ready to go home. Little did I know that this next patient would be the spark for a twenty-plus year project of collecting stories for this book.

I saw on the chart that I was seeing a child named James who was complaining of ear pain. James was a five-year-old and the shyest child I had ever met. In the three previous visits we'd had, I had never heard him speak. He would always look down when I addressed him. His mom told me he was like that with everybody. Even though I was exhausted, I was determined to get this child to speak to me. I told him jokes and tried every trick I knew but could not break through his shell.

I eventually gave up and told his mom he did indeed have an ear infection. I explained to her that I was going to give him Augmentin, a very strong antibiotic.

I like this antibiotic because it almost always works, but many parents do not like it because of the side effects. Augmentin kills good bacteria as well as bad and therefore often causes diarrhea or yeast infections and because of this, many people eat yogurt when they are on this medicine to replenish their good bacteria.

On hearing I was going to give him Augmentin, she said, "Please don't give him that. It gives him a rash in his privates."

I replied, "Well, you can get him some yogurt."

The words were still hanging in the air when a miracle happened. My little patient abruptly looked up and yelled, "I gotta put yogurt on my privates?!"

As I got over my shock that he had spoken in front of me, I absorbed what he had said. Mom and I laughed for a good couple of minutes. He seemed relieved when we explained that *eating* yogurt would help prevent a rash on his privates.

Two things happened that day. First, I went straight out and bought a tape recorder to keep track of funny stories such as this. Second, I learned that no matter how bad a day I was having, these wonderful patients of mine could make it all better with one sentence!

Since that day, I have kept the tape recorder in my car and on the way home from work, I recorded funny stories from my day. Finally, after mentally nagging myself for years, I have written these stories down on paper for others to enjoy.

What you are about to read is the accumulation of stories gathered over my twenty-eight years of practicing pediatrics. Many of the stories originate from the mouths of the amateur comedians who are my patients. Some are from their parents and families. There are also many of my not-so-great moments when I inserted my foot directly into my mouth.

My goal in writing this book is twofold. First, to make you laugh, and to tell you about events that have made me laugh. Second, to give you an inside look at what it is like to be a pediatrician in a small town.

Actually, the first time I thought about writing a book was when I was fourteen years old and read *All Creatures Great and Small* by James Herriot. The book is about the real-life experiences of a country veterinarian in England in the 1930s. At that point in my life, I was sure I was going to be a vet and I loved that the book gave me a behind-the-scenes glimpse of what it was like to take care of animals. I decided then that I would write a similar book when I became a vet.

Life has a way of changing one's plans and I became a doctor of children instead of animals (in many ways they really aren't that different!).

Truthfully, even though I thought I would write a book when I was older, I lacked two things. As most of my teachers would attest, I am not a very skilled writer. And secondly, I do not really enjoy writing. I am much more comfortable telling stories in person so I can see the smiles and hear the laughter as I hit the punchline. Plus, I really enjoy mimicking voices, which I have not figured out how to do in print form.

However, my job has been filled with so many hilarious children, unpredictable parents, and verbal gaffes on my part, it seemed a travesty not to document them.

I want to be clear that it is not my intention to belittle or make fun of people, but merely to describe the events as they happened. I share a special bond with my patients and their families. I am there with them in the good times and the bad and I would never intentionally hurt their feelings. What's more, I begrudgingly admit that the chapter of me saying the wrong thing is one of the longest in the book.

Rest assured that every name in the book has been changed—partly "to protect the innocent" and partly because I have trouble remembering people's names.

I do want to add one additional caveat. Pediatricians use the titles "mom" and "dad" very freely throughout our day. We have thousands of patients and it is impossible to learn everyone's parents' names. In the stories, those generic titles will be used often.

Why should you read this book? To have a nice laugh! My grandmother always told me when I was young that laughter was good for your health. I have never forgotten that and try to balance the stress of my job with daily laughs. I hope these funny insights into the life of a pediatrician make you laugh and improve your day.

So, sit back and enjoy the best stories from my twenty-eight years of caring for children.

HOWDY!

FUNNY KIDS

One of the best things about being a pediatrician is the nonstop entertainment provided by the children. Kids see things vastly differently from adults and I love to hear their take on the world. Children also tend to lack a filter and will often verbalize any thought that comes into their heads. Both of these tendencies lead to hilarious situations. I feel very fortunate that I get to spend my day with people who can turn any situation into a comedy.

Shortly after deciding to write this book, I had an unforgettable experience with a very anxious nine-year-old girl named Maggie. I had known her since she was born and always found her to be quite timid and full of questions. On this occasion, I was seeing her for a well visit and I had just finished checking her privates and announced to her mom that there were no signs of puberty.

Maggie's eyes became very wide and she said, "Puberty! What is puberty?"

I always pride myself on modeling my physician style after Andy Griffith. If "Opie" asks me a question, I am going to answer it. So, I told her that puberty is when your body goes through some changes.

Her eyes got even bigger and she asked, "What kind of changes?"

I never saw Andy deal with this subject, but I was sure if faced with such a question, he would give a truthful answer. Therefore, I replied, "Hair is going to grow on different parts of your body."

At this point Maggie was obviously starting to become upset and she blurted out, "Where is the hair going to grow?"

I could see out of the corner of my eye her mom starting to shake her head, but I was too far in to stop so I told her, "On your privates where I just checked you."

She literally screamed, "How am I going to get it off?"

I quickly told her it was normal and that she didn't need to remove it.

She then turned to her mom and asked, "How do you get yours off?"

There was an awkward silence as I watched her mom's face turn a color of purple rarely seen in humans. Her mom started to explain how she removes it when I stopped her mid-sentence. I told her that discussion was probably best had in private between just the two of them.

I am sure her mom wished the entire conversation had been in private. This experience taught me a very important lesson in finding a way to reply to awkward questions: "Your mom will explain that to you later."

Over the years, I have been called many funny names by my young patients who have trouble remembering Benfield. These include Dr. Bean Field, Dr. Field, and, occasionally, Dr. Phil. I always put a stop to this last one for obvious reasons. I even had a patient who always called me Dr. Brown Bear, although he would not tell me why.

My favorite nickname was from a small, shy four-year-old boy. When I walked in to see him, he kept whispering to his mom, "Is that Dr. Said?"

The mom apologized to me and explained. "He thinks that's your name because every night he makes us read to him the book, *Five Little Monkeys Jumping on the Bed.*

I still didn't understand until she quoted the story to me. "Five little monkeys jumping on the bed, one fell off and bumped his head, Mama called the doctor, and the *doctor said*..."

I pointed at the little boy and continued, "No more monkeys jumping on the bed!" I was instantly his hero.

One of the funniest age groups that I see in my office are the toddlers. Everything is new to them and this perspective often makes them say outlandish things. One of my favorite toddler stories involves a two-year-old named David.

I was seeing him with his parents and his four-month-old brother. Often, adding a new baby to a family can make a toddler regress in behavior and I was asking the parents if this had happened to David. They reported not at all, that he really seemed to like his little brother.

Then the dad said, "It's kind of funny; David thinks the baby's name is Easy. He walks around calling him Easy."

I thought this was a bit weird and asked the dad why.

"Well, because whenever he gets near him, we tell him, 'Easy, easy.' And so now, whenever David sees him, that's what he says, 'Easy, easy.'"

So, of course, as the baby grew up and I saw him in the office, I always referred to him as Easy.

Another one of my favorite toddlers was named Joshua. Joshua was a future comedian in the making and always made me laugh during our visits. One summer day, I was seeing him for his three-year-old checkup. On this visit, we usually ask children to provide a urine sample.

When I went in to see him, he was so proud and said, "I peed in a cup! I peed in a cup!"

I congratulated him and noticed mom was smiling and shaking her head. I knew immediately that there was more to the story.

She informed me that after he peed in the cup and she was screwing the lid on the cup, she heard him kind of grunt. So, she asked him, "Do you have to go poo-poo?"

He replied with a huge grin on his face, "Yeah, I do. Can I poop in that cup?"

His mom thought this was mildly amusing, but I thought it was hilarious. I have always felt my sense of humor was stuck at a seventh-grade level. Maybe that's why I get along with my patients so well.

Speaking of collecting urine samples, one of my patient's moms had a very unpleasant experience with this part of the visit. During the winter of 2010, our office installed new lights in the bathrooms to save energy. The lights are motion sensitive and turn off when no one is in the bathroom. Unfortunately, we aimed the motion sensors too high, causing a mom to get an unwelcome shower.

I found this out as I entered a patient room to find the mom with a paper towel trying to dry off the front of her shirt. She reported that when she bent down in front of her four-year-old son to collect a urine specimen in a cup, the lights went out mid-stream. She said she was moving the cup with one hand trying to guess where the urine was and waving her other arm in the air trying to make the lights go back on, all while screaming, "Stop peeing!"

I asked the little boy what he did and he smiled and said, "I kept peeing!"

This was obvious as it looked like mom had a perfect Z drawn across her chest that would have made Zorro proud. We fixed the sensors that day!

As I am constantly surrounded by little comedians, I often feel the urge to add some funny one-liners myself. Sometimes my quick wit is not appreciated as was the case with this next young male who was not in the mood for my humor. I was sitting at my desk when the boy, who looked to be about ten, walked up and asked me where the bathroom was.

"We don't have any bathrooms. But we do have a pee bucket."

He gave me an exacerbated look and replied, "Well, where is the pee bucket?"

Even though all siblings are competitive, I find twins are often the most competitive as they are constantly trying to assert their individualism. This led to a funny situation when I was seeing two five-year-old identical twins who were arguing about who was the best soccer player.

Things predictably escalated and Max said, "Well, you may grow up to be the better player, but you will always be the ugliest guy on the team!"

This led to Jackson bursting into tears and his mom telling Max to be nice.

I stared at both Max and his mom waiting for them to see the humor in this statement. They are identical twins! Neither of them got it and I finished the visit proud of myself for, once in my life, not making a situation worse with my big mouth.

In the movies, identical twins often switch places to fool people, but I didn't think that really happened until my nurse, Kelsey, told me about her twin boys' escapades in kindergarten.

It started with Kelsey receiving a call from the school nurse saying she was surprised Rhett was at school that day as he had been in her office the day before after having had a small diarrheal accident in his pants at school.

Kelsey was confused as Rhett's identical twin brother, Reed, had been the one to come home from school in different underwear the day before. Later that night, Kelsey asked Reed if he had an accident at school.

"Yes. I was trying to fart, but something else came out too."

She then said, "Well, why did the nurse think you were Rhett?"

He replied, "I was embarrassed, so I told her I was Rhett."

At that point, Rhett, who was in the shower and overheard the conversation, swung the curtain aside and angrily yelled, "What!?"

Like most pediatricians, I see many children with autism. These are interesting kids to take care of and no two are alike. Some don't understand humor, and others, because of their lack of a verbal filter, say the funniest things. I was seeing one of my high-functioning autistic patients named Kevin for his ten-year-old wellness check and I mentioned autism. His younger brother looked up and said, "Do you still have autism?"

He replied sarcastically, "No, I pooped the puzzle piece out!"

For those who aren't aware, the symbol for autism is a colorful puzzle piece. Mom and I laughed. I was so proud of Kevin's progress.

On another occasion, I was seeing another autistic patient, Leo, who has a much more severe condition with a habit of repeating things he hears over and over. He had just turned thirteen and his mom was concerned about how long he was staying in the bathroom. I suggested that maybe he was constipated.

She leaned close to me and whispered, "I think he is choking the chicken."

David overheard this and started screaming at the top of his lungs, "Choking the chicken. Choking the chicken!"

It took a minute for us to get him to stop. Once the visit was over, I stepped out of the room to find three nurses and two doctors waiting for me with concerned looks on their faces. I shrugged my shoulders and quickly went into the next room. Sometimes there are just no explanations.

Some of my favorite stories happen because children can be a bit too literal at times. This was the case with a seven-year-old patient named Miles who was in my office for an ear infection. After telling her about the infection, I asked the mom if she wanted me to write a prescription for pills or liquid.

She started laughing and answered. "Liquid, as long as he doesn't dance with it like last time."

I asked what she meant and she told Miles to tell me what he did.

A blushing Miles said, "I read the bottle and it said 'Shake well before using' so I started shaking all over!"

Another one of my other patients had some confusion over a medicine bottle as well. A mom reported to me that she found her six-year-old daughter trying to open an ibuprofen bottle.

The little girl asked, "Why can't I open this?"

Her mom explained, "Because it is a childproof bottle."

"How does it know I am a child?"

One of the most common things parents want to discuss at well visits is, not surprisingly, their child's behavior. On one memorable day, I was seeing a three-year-old little girl named Abby. Her mom was asking my advice for some behavioral issues Abby was having.

I looked down at this smiling, freckled face and said, "This sweet child has behavioral issues?"

The mom replied, "Don't let that face fool you, she can be a little demon."

I patted Abby on her head and told her mom, "She looks like an angel to me."

Her mom said, "Let me tell you what this *angel* did this morning. I found a half-eaten piece of melted chocolate in my bed. So, I went to Abby and asked her if she put anything in my bed. Do you want to know what she said to me?"

I meekly nodded yes.

The mom looked at Abby and reported, "She said, 'I didn't put chocolate in your bed!'"

I looked down at Abby, who gave me a mischievous grin, and I admitted to Mom, "Okay. So, she is not *always* an angel."

Whenever I do an x-ray of a child, I like to pull up their film on the computer and show it to them. They are always amazed by this and often have funny things to say about it.

I had one six-year-old look at his chest x-ray and scream, "I have a skeleton?"

My favorite response was from a three-year-old male. I took an x-ray of his abdomen because of his complaints that his belly hurt. The x-ray showed severe constipation, as I suspected.

I pointed to an area on the x-ray and told the child, "This area is your stomach and if you look down here you can see all this poop backed up. This is why your stomach hurts."

The child looked alarmed and said loudly, "I have not been eating poop! I promise!"

I know that many children are anxious during their visits, so I have come up with many techniques to try to make them relax. One of my favorites is pretending I can feel what they have been eating when I am palpating their abdomen (feeling their tummy).

Many of my patients love this game and will say things like, "You are never going to guess what I ate today!" and then scream in delight when I get it wrong.

I even had one patient who would eat odd things before his appointment because he didn't want me to guess correctly. By the way, if I guess "chicken nuggets," I am right seventy-five percent of the time. Guessing pizza on Friday afternoons has a 99 percent correct rate.

One of my funniest experiences using this technique came with a ten-year-old boy who was not happy to be at the doctor's office. As I examined his abdomen I said, "You have been eating pizza. I can feel it right here."

He shook his head and replied, "I haven't had pizza in two weeks!"

Trying to make him laugh I said, "Then you need to go poop! That pizza has been in there too long!"

He suddenly became concerned and looked over to his dad to ask, "Can we stop at the bathroom on the way out?"

After correctly guessing pizza on one of my four-year-old patients, I decided to take it further and said that it felt like pepperoni pizza.

He replied, "I hate pepperoni! I only eat plain pizza!"

So, I asked him if there was anything he liked on pizza.

He said, "Well, I like Farmer John cheese."

I asked, "What kind of cheese?"

He said, "Farmer John cheese."

I looked around and said, "I don't understand what that is. What kind of cheese is that?"

And his mom started laughing. "That's what he calls Parmesan cheese," she told me. And from that day on, that is what I call it as well.

One of the most difficult tasks a parent is faced with is potty training. Over the years, I have heard many descriptions of how they accomplished it, but never quite like the following little girl's description.

Her name was Mia and I was seeing her for a three-year well check with her dad.

Her dad and I were having a tough time holding down a conversation as Mia wanted to interject something every few moments. She was very smart for her age and had a nice vocabulary, but, like most three-year-old kids, she had little patience for being left out of a conversation.

At one point, dad said, "We finally got her potty trained."

"Great," I replied. "How did you get her to do it?"

Dad was getting ready to tell me when the little girl blurted out, "I pull down my panties and then I put my bottom on the big girl toilet ..."

We stopped her before she got any further, but if I'm going to ask a question, I guess I should be prepared for the answer.

Living in North Carolina I am blessed to hear some of the best Southern accents. One day, I was talking with an eight-year-old boy named Jackson and I asked where he was from.

He replied with a very thick Southern accent, "Shelby," but he pronounced it "Shelllll-bee," somehow managing to make one word last two seconds.

This made me chuckle and I told him I liked the way he spoke.

He said, "Yeah, a lot of my friends talk Western like I do."

Confused, I asked, "What, are you a cowboy?"

And he replied, "No, I just speak Western."

Then it hit me, "Oh! You mean Southern."

And he said, "Yeah, yeah, that's what I mean, Southern. Sometimes I get those two mixed up."

The fact that small children are apt to say anything is not always a good thing for me. Sometimes, they say things like "your ears have hair in them" or "your shoes look old." The moms are always embarrassed and scold them, but I tell them truthfully that it doesn't bother me as this is the nature of kids.

There was one visit, however, when a three-year-old girl's comment really did hurt my feelings. I was seeing her for a bad cough and I asked the mom if she had ever wheezed. The mom replied that she wheezes every time she gets a cold.

I turned to the little girl and said, "So, you are a little wheezer?"

She angrily replied, "I am not a wheezer!" Then, with the tone and expression of a girl ten years older, she added, "Weirdo!"

That one stuck with me for a couple of days.

On occasion, my patients make me laugh even when they are mad at me. I had just finished seeing a four-year-old girl for a well visit and she was upset because she had just received three vaccines.

As she was leaving, she gave me a dirty look. I sweetly said, "See you next time."

She looked at her mom and screamed, "I have to come back?"

As technology has advanced, parents have had to become versed in an entirely new language. Words like cloud, stream, and viral now have very different meanings than when we were young. This was very evident to me when I was seeing an eight-year-old male with an ear infection.

I told mom I was going to give him an antibiotic and asked if he could take a tablet or would he need a liquid form.

His eyes lit up and he said, "Hey, I got a tablet for Christmas!"

Just like that, I lost one of my most used medical terms. Now, I only ask if the patient can take a pill.

One would think that after all these years taking care of children that I would be prepared for anything they may say. However, as these next two children prove, I continue to be surprised with what comes out of their mouths.

A six-year-old boy named Anthony had obviously been waiting to see me to get some of his questions answered.

I had not been in the room long when he raised his hand.

I thought this was adorable and asked, “Do you have something to say?”

He said, “Yeah, I do.”

He then started making some strange hand gestures, as if he was showing me the size of something. He finally clarified this by asking, “How long should a person’s penis be?”

His mom’s eyes got really big and she shouted, “Anthony!”

I told her it was fine since I asked if he had a question.

He went on to say, “Because I measured it and …”

This time both mom and I yelled “Anthony!”

I then changed the subject before he could finish.

At the end of the visit, I asked him if he had any *non-penis* questions.

He got a sneaky look in his eye and said, “Well …”

His mom put a stop to what was to follow with, “No Anthony!”

He then looked down sadly and said, “No sir.”

Part of me was relieved, but the other part was curious as to what he was going to ask this time.

A seven-year-old named Aaron caught me off guard because of his unusual imagination. I was seeing him for a well check up and asked him how he was doing in school.

He looked at me confidently and said, "I am doing great. Thomas gives me all the answers!"

I looked to his mom for an explanation but she only smiled and nodded proudly.

"Does your teacher know Thomas is giving you the answers?"

Now his mom decided to explain, "Thomas is not a person. Thomas is what he calls his brain."

Are you beginning to see why I enjoy treating kids and not adults?

No matter how busy I get in the clinic I can always count on a child to make me stop and smile.

A great example of this was one winter day when I was feeling a bit overwhelmed by how many patients I had seen with high fevers and flu symptoms. My last patient before lunch was a precocious three-year-old girl named Morgan.

She was there with a cough and I was having a tough time getting the history as she was trying her best to keep my attention on her instead of her mom. She repeatedly called out my name only to have nothing to say when I would turn to her. Finally, after hearing my name ten times in a row, I stopped what I was doing and waited, giving her my full attention.

I could see her brain racing to come up with something and she finally said, "Dr. Benfield, I hurt my lip. Look at it."

I looked at her lip and there was a tiny sore on it.

I said, "Oh, Morgan, I am so sorry."

She took my hand and gave me the sweetest look and she said, "No, no, you didn't do it."

I took a deep breath, smiled, and mentally reminded myself how fortunate I am to work with children.

ARE YOU FUNNIER THAN A KINDERGARTENER?

Ask any pediatrician which age group is the funniest and they will all answer the same: the kindergarteners! Every age group is funny in their own way. Toddlers are amusing because of their innocent view of life, middle schoolers are experts at using potty humor, and teens love to use their sharp, sarcastic wit to cut into their victims.

But no group makes me laugh as hard and as often as the kindergarteners. These kids say whatever comes into their heads. They lack the social awareness to know that what they are saying may be a bit inappropriate. It is because of this age that I always try to have fresh breath. A five-year-old child will look you right in the eye and tell you your breath stinks.

Every year, in July and August, we have "Kindergarten Days" where our entire schedule is reserved for four- and five-year-olds who need a physical before starting school. These are cherished times as I love spending an entire day with my favorite age group.

The kindergarten visit is also special because this is usually the first visit where the child is old enough that I can direct most of my questions to them instead of their parents. This leads to some hilarious answers.

During one of these events, I met Dylan, a cute five-year-old boy who I was meeting for the first time. This was during the good old days when I had paper charts. I noticed his chart had a stamp on it that said there were two patients in the clinic with the same first and last names.

So, I asked him, "Dylan, is your birthday June 3, 1996?" After he confirmed this, I explained to his dad that our clinic had two Dylan McMillans and I just wanted to make sure I had the right chart.

Dylan looked very concerned and asked, "There's two of me?"

I explained, "Not like a twin. There's just somebody else with your same name."

And he looked relieved and I said, "You have different birthdays so I can tell you apart."

His eyes lit up and he exclaimed, "I know how you can tell us apart. I've got a mama and her name is Mrs. McMillan."

I told him that was helpful, but I would stick with the birthday technique.

I have found that many of the kids in the four- to five-year-old age group are nervous at their visit because they are often due for shots. Fortunately, I have different techniques for getting their minds off the coming injections. One of my favorites is to ask them their age followed by asking them if they are married.

They usually laugh and look at their parents like, "Is this guy for real?" However, sometimes this joke fails to connect. A nervous four-year-old male came in for his kindergarten visit and I asked, "Are you married?"

And he said, "No, I'm Joshua!" Okay, so maybe he was a bit young for that joke.

Another one of my techniques to put kids at ease is to walk in the room, look at their chart and say, "It says here you are here to talk about girls (or boys if the patient is a girl)."

When the patients are girls, they usually smile or laugh shyly. The boys, however, do not think it is funny. Some ball up their fist and shake it at me. Some yell at their mom, thinking she made an appointment for that. Occasionally, a boy will even start crying.

However, on one occasion, one of my male patients surprised me by saying, "I do want to talk about girls!"

I played along and asked him what he wanted to know about them.

He smiled broadly and said, "Everything!"

I didn't have the heart to tell him I didn't really know that much myself.

As I mentioned, this age group sees the world differently than the rest of us. I try to remember this when taking their history.

Children of this age are also quick to tell you if you do something they do not like. I once had a five-year-old put me in my place as I was examining her newborn brother.

At one point during the exam, I turned the baby over and held him facing downward so I could look at the back of his head.

The little girl pointed at me with wide eyes and said, "You are not supposed to hold him like that!"

One challenging thing about this age group is that they are now old enough to learn how to manipulate their parents. It is no coincidence that this is a common age for children to start inventing symptoms to get out of doing stuff, especially going to school.

This next kindergartener was a master of this technique. Her name was Evie and I was talking to her mom about her recurrent complaints of pain.

"One day she will complain about her foot hurting and the next day it will be her elbow. We never see any redness or swelling."

I gently asked her mom if she thought maybe the child was saying these things to get attention.

The little girl made my case for me when she piped up with, "I don't want attention! I just want my pain juice!"

It turns out that every time she complained she received a dose of ibuprofen (pain juice).

After further questioning, Evie admitted that she loved the way it tasted.

The mom put her hand on her head and exclaimed, "Oh Lord. I have created a little drug addict!"

Simple questions with this age group can take on an entirely different meaning, as with this five-year-old, Alyssa. She came in with fever and abdominal pain. I was getting details about her pain and asked her, "Sweetie, where does your stomach hurt?"

She looked at me without even blinking and said, "At home."

Sometimes you need to see the world through the eyes of a child. Alyssa wasn't trying to be funny; her stomach *did* hurt at home.

I rephrased the question: "Show me where on your belly it hurts."

She didn't respond, so a little bit later, after I had finished taking my history and was getting ready to examine her, I lifted her shirt. I asked again, "Now, where does your stomach hurt?"

And she screamed, "At home!"

Sometimes I am a little slow to catch on.

I had another miscommunication with a kindergartener named Oliver who looked angry when I walked into the room for his annual well visit. He was holding his finger and he said, "Why did you take my blood?"

"Because we have to test it."

His eyes got really big and he covered his mouth, "Taste it! You drank my blood?!"

I told him I said "test" and reassured him I was not a vampire and then showed him his results on the computer.

His mom then said, "Tell Dr. Benfield what you were worried they did with your blood when we first got into the room."

He looked at me seriously and said, "I think you are trying to clone me!"

I laughed and promised him I could only handle one version of him. To which his mom added, "Amen!"

I love watching parents' faces become anxious when kindergarteners start talking about their homelife. The fear that the child will say something inappropriate is ever present.

I once asked a mom if her child had ever had any blood in the urine and before she could answer, her son piped up with, "I haven't, but my mom has! I have seen it in the toilet."

Based on the look on his mom's face, I think she was questioning her decision to become a parent. They don't teach you how to reply to things like that in medical school.

I had a similar experience when I was talking to a five-year-old male named Elijah about staying in his yard. His mom was very concerned about his safety and so I was giving him a stern lecture about the dangers of leaving his home by himself.

He defiantly replied, "But I like exploring by myself!"

I kiddingly told him, "We are going to have to make you wear one of those dog shock collars."

His eyes got big. Then he started laughing before asking, "It would shock me if I left the yard?"

I added, "Absolutely. Not a bad shock. Just enough to make you pee a little."

He immediately spouted, "My mom pees a little when she sneezes!"

Mom's face went scarlet but then she shrugged her shoulders and admitted, "He's not wrong."

My next filterless kindergartener goes by Stuart. He is destined to become a comedian. He has a twin brother who is equally as funny. On one occasion, I was seeing the boys for a wellness visit and their mother was complaining about their behavior.

At one point she said, "You can't imagine how out of control they are. They don't listen and they have no manners." She illustrated this by telling me, "I went into their room yesterday and there was a big booger smeared on the wall."

Stuart looked up and said, "Mom, that wasn't me. You know I eat mine."

Sometimes, the inappropriate things that children say don't make me laugh but instead make me uncomfortable. When this happens, I just keep staring at my computer and pretend I did not hear them. This was never truer than when I complimented a four-year-old girl on the dress she was wearing.

She looked down at her dress and replied proudly, "Thanks. My mom stole it from Walmart!"

I did not see her mom's reaction as my computer had never seemed so interesting.

My clinic used to have a system to see patients when all the schedules were full. The patients were booked on a "Dr. Any" schedule, meaning the patient would see whichever provider could get to them first. It was a great way to see patients the same day instead of putting them off until the next. When one of these patients arrived in the clinic, our front desk would alert the nurses in the back by paging "Any 100?"

One staff member noticed that every time they used this page, a five-year-old patient in the waiting room would yell, "I am!"

When my nurse went to get him, he told her, "I am hungry."

She didn't know what to say but told him she was sure his mom would get him something to eat when they left. It was only after he left that we figured out he was hearing "Anyone hungry?" when we paged. Which is, naturally, what I hear now, every time they page "Any 100?"

Another memorable five-year-old visit occurred with a little girl who happened to be one of my neighbors. I noticed that she was wearing a shirt with the words "Rainbow Connection" on the front, which was the name of her preschool.

I jokingly said, "Sweetie, you're in kindergarten now. Isn't it embarrassing to wear a shirt that says the name of your preschool on it?"

"No," she replied. "None of my friends can read."

Asking a kindergartener what they want to be when they grow up can reveal some interesting career goals. Gone are the days when the most popular answer was NBA or NFL star, nurse, or teacher. Now, the most common answer is YouTuber, video game creator, or TikToker.

Although there are times when I have the literal children who answer "grown" or "an adult."

Recently, I had a sweet little girl saying she wanted to be a babysitter so she could sing to the babies.

On a not-so-sweet note, one little boy told me he wanted to grow up and be a scammer. I stared at him for a second and then decided not to ask any follow-up questions.

Some of my kindergarteners still have classic goals, like the girl who told me she wanted to be a teacher. I liked her answer and so quizzed her further by asking what age group she would like to teach.

She replied, "I am not sure, but definitely not kindergarteners."

When I asked why, she added, "Because I don't like little kids."

Personally, I could not disagree more. I am now considering opening a new specialized pediatric clinic that only sees ages four to six!

FUNNY MOMS

WHEN I FIRST DECIDED TO PUT my experiences on tape, I thought my stories would only be about children being funny. I had no idea how often I would find humor in the parents. Moms are the ones who usually bring the children to visits and they are often funnier than the kids.

I would be remiss in starting a chapter about moms without pointing out the critical role they play in bringing up children. Behind every successful person is a mom who showed them the way. I am not one to quote famous people, but I like the following piece of brilliance by Rudyard Kipling, "God could not be everywhere, and therefore he made mothers."

I often leave visits thinking *thank goodness for moms.* I am in awe of all the sacrifices they make for their children because, as is often stated, there is no harder job than being a mom.

Being a pediatrician, there are often days when I see a very sick child or a sad social situation and these cases cause me to go home a bit depressed. Thankfully, I have more days when I sit down with a wonderful mom who makes me laugh or smile. This chapter goes out to all the moms who brightened my day with the funny things they said, either intentionally or often unintentionally.

Once a mom and I were laughing at the chaos that was her life raising four small children and she said, "Well, I can either laugh or I can cry."

On another occasion, I asked a mom at her newborn visit if she was experiencing any post-partum depression.

She replied, "I have five children. I do not have time to be depressed."

Some moms are funny because of what they don't know about raising kids, but this mom was funny because she had parenting figured out! I was seeing her two-year-old boy for a well visit and asked her, "Do you brush your child's teeth?"

She said, "Yeah, but it takes some bribery."

"What do you mean?"

She replied, "Well, he hates to have his teeth brushed, so every night I give him a dollar to get him to brush his teeth."

I was a bit surprised by this. "Oh, Mom, every night you give him a dollar?" I asked.

She said, "I know. It's not great."

"Well, goodness that's expensive," I replied.

She countered with, "Oh no, it's the same dollar every night."

I went from thinking this mom was spoiling her child and needed some guidance to quickly realizing she was a genius! I do feel a little sorry for the child though, who probably thinks he is rich, but only has one dollar.

During my training I was taught to always end a visit with, "Do you have any other questions for me?"

Usually the parent responds with, "No, I think we have covered it."

However, sometimes this is when I get my funniest questions. Like the time a mom came to see me one summer morning with her fifteen-month-old son, Alex. Alex was doing great and at the end of the visit, I asked his mom if she had any other concerns.

After some hesitation she said, "Well, you know, I've got one concern. I don't know if I want to bring it up."

I assured her she could ask me anything.

So, she did, "His poop really stinks."

"Well, Mom, poop really stinks," was the brilliant reply that came out of my mouth before I realized what I was saying. Obviously, she was worried there was something wrong with him because he had a significant foul odor to his stool.

But I did not understand the degree of odor she was describing until she said, "It smells so bad that when we are changing his diaper, the dog scratches on the door and whines to go outside!"

One of the things people hate about coming to the doctor is the waiting. What most people don't know is that doctors hate to leave people waiting. Trust me, there are no coffee breaks. If your doctor is not with you, they are with another patient or on the computer writing a note on another patient.

On one busy winter day, I was running behind more than usual. As soon as I walked into my patient's room I started apologizing. The patient was fifteen months old, and so I knew the mom's wait could not have been much fun.

Surprisingly, she smiled up at me and said, "You don't need to apologize. My husband is home with our four other children. I have enjoyed my one-on-one time with my daughter." She then added, "Plus, it is good for my husband to see what I go through every day."

I jokingly told her I could go back out for fifteen more minutes and she put her hand up and said, "No, we have had a good time, but we are ready for the visit."

Some moms are funny because of their bluntness. They are going to get their point across even if it is embarrassing. I was seeing one such mom with her husband for their newborn's first visit. The baby was significantly smaller than expected for a term baby and I asked the mom if she was sure about the due date.

She replied, "Well, when you only have sex once per year, you know your dates exactly."

I tried not to blush at this announcement and simply said, "Fair enough," and quickly changed the subject. Dad however, did not look up for the rest of the visit.

One of my favorite types of moms is the "proud" mom. This type wants me to be as proud of her child as she is. I find this endearing; however, I had one mom who took this approach too far.

Whenever I did a well visit on her son, John, she spent the entire visit telling me about how wonderful he was. I was barely allowed to speak.

She had a funny way of describing him. For example, at his three-year-old well check she said, "He is the smartest child in his daycare. I think he may be a genius."

What made me internally chuckle is she whispered the word "genius" to me, as if his intelligence was a secret and she didn't want him to know about it.

Later, she described him as "scary smart." Again, whispered!

I then realized we were out of time and I had not asked her a single question since she had spent the entire visit singing his praises. So, I asked her, "Is there anything going on with John that I can help you with?"

She thought for a second and then said, "Yes, there is one thing he does that worries us." She went on to tell me that every time he took a bath he would poop in the tub! They even had purchased a special net to fish it out.

It took every ounce of willpower I had not to whisper "genius!"

Speaking of being proud, no one is prouder of a child than their grandparents. All parents are proud of their children, but grandparents take it to an entirely new level. I love to see their eyes light up when they describe their grandchildren's latest accomplishments. It can, however, make well visits more challenging when the grandparents want to spend the entire appointment gushing about them.

I have had many visits where mom and I are discussing something about the child's health and I can see the grandparent leaning forward with a big smile on their face.

As soon as there is the tiniest pause in the conversation, they will interject, "Did you know he knows his colors?" or "She is fourth chair on the clarinet in the band!"

I even had one grandmother tell me with a very proud look in her eye, "My grandson has beaten every level in the *Call of Duty* video game!"

I can't wait to be a grandparent, so I can appreciate this level of passion about a child's accomplishments.

Right before I finished this book, I had a late addition that fits perfectly in this chapter. I was chatting with a new couple about their one-month-old baby. During their first visit right after the baby was born, I had told them a funny story and went on to tell them that I was writing a book about the many amusing experiences I've had throughout my career.

At this visit, mom was telling me that the baby's umbilical cord stump had fallen off and she didn't think it looked right. For those of you who have never had a child, right after birth, the umbilical cord is cut and then clamped close to the baby's belly. After two to three weeks, this "stump" then falls off, leaving the belly button we are all used to seeing.

The dad then piped up, "She wanted to bring the cord stump with us and show you, but I told her we would end up in your book!" He was correct.

milK

DAD, AKA "THE MAN WITH THE LIST"

As a pediatrician, I spend most of my time interacting with moms. Sometimes, the mom and dad come in together and these are my favorite visits. I like having dad's perspective and being able to tell him all the stuff I usually only tell the mom. Dads are more of a blank slate and anything you tell them is usually something they have never heard before.

Occasionally, because of work and scheduling conflicts, the dad brings the child to the well visit. Unfortunately, in many cases, this is a pretty worthless visit. Fathers typically do not know as much about the ins and outs of children as moms do. For example, I usually don't get a good history of what the child eats or when they sleep, or details about their developmental milestones from the dad, so it can be very frustrating.

The pure comic relief that dads can bring, however, make these visits highly entertaining. Early in my career I toyed with the idea of requiring dads to pass a simple three question quiz about their children before they would be allowed to bring them alone.

Did I mention the lists? Many times, when I see a dad alone with a child, he will pull out a list. Basically, it is a list of questions from the mom. I usually write the answers on the paper because if mom can't trust him to ask the right questions, how can I trust him to remember the answers?

Many of these are comical in their detail. "Hand the insurance card to the lady at the desk," or "Don't forget to take the diaper bag." These types of dads are about as helpful as if a taxi driver brought in the child.

Now, with advancing technology, I see a different kind of dad who I call "The cell phone holder dad." During these visits, as soon as I walk in the door, the dad will get his wife on the phone via Facetime. He will then hold the phone up as the mother of the child and I go through the visit.

To be fair, with more women being the primary breadwinners, I am seeing a lot of stay-at-home dads. These types of dads are awesome and do a great job with the kids. The visits are very different as these dads tend to focus on how a child is doing right now. They ask very few questions about what could go wrong.

In general, I find that dads don't seem to worry about the "what ifs" as much as moms do. When it comes to being involved in every part of a child's life, however, you can't beat a mom. There is very little that moms do not know about a child. Generally speaking, I would always rather obtain a history from a mom.

Back to the lists. I remember one dad who arrived with a list, which usually is good, except in this case it was a very detailed list. It was a front- and back-filled notebook-sized page of questions from mom. There were twenty questions, each with a small space after the question so that dad could write the answer down.

Dad's statement to me was, "I married a rational woman. When I married her, she was rational, she was normal." He went on, "Ever since we have had this child, she has the most irrational fears and worries I have ever seen. She is making me do this."

He asked me, "Please, write down the answers. I won't be able to remember all that you say."

I went through the list, what I considered to be an essay test of mom's questions, and boy, it was a doozy. Dad was right.

One question was: "My child has a rash that sometimes appears that seems to get worse when he is in the sun. Could he be allergic to sunlight?"

Second question: "My child has a wide space between his first and second toe. Is this harmful and is there surgery to correct this?"

Third question: "My child's head is shaped funny. Is there anything that we can do? I am afraid he is going to be made fun of in middle school."

So, this list was going on and on and I took basically the entire visit to sit and painstakingly write in the answers. We didn't get to do anything else. I did manage to examine the child, but there was nothing else we really talked about. That is what mom wanted out of the visit and that is what she got, so she was happy, I am sure.

Of course, not all dads bring lists. One morning, I was talking to a dad about his six-month-old boy, and asked him to tell me about his child's development. Dad had an excited look in his eyes and said, "He's starting to crawl, he's babbling, he can track with his eyes, and he can watch TV."

It was endearing to see how impressed dad was with his baby and I complimented the baby's accomplishments.

Then dad said the oddest thing. "I forgot. He can also smack people with things!"

I replied, "What do you mean?"

And he said, "Well, he takes things and hits people with them."

I said, "Really?"

And dad was just grinning from ear to ear. "And that's his best thing!" he told me proudly.

I was impressed that the child was beginning to crawl and babble, but dad was proud that he could take objects and use them as weapons against other people.

When a parent says something funny by mistake, I often have to remind myself that I am a professional and make sure that my amusement stays hidden. However, there are times that despite my best efforts, there is no way to restrain my laughter.

On one such occasion, I was seeing a dad with his preteen daughter for a well visit. She had undergone a large amount of orthodontic work and her father was proudly showing me the results.

He said, "You see this tooth here? It came in backwards and they had to rotate it 360 degrees!"

"Yes," I laughed. I think I even held my stomach as I did it. They both looked at me confused and, not wanting to embarrass him, I told him I thought the image of the tooth spinning was funny.

One of my techniques to help parents with babies that won't sleep is to switch the baby monitors around so that they have the speaking end and they can talk to the baby and calm them down without getting up. I suggested this to a couple with a five-month-old once and the dad's eyes got really big and he exclaimed, "We can't do that!"

When I asked him why not, he replied, "Ours is a video monitor and I don't want the baby to see what goes on in the bedroom!"

I took a deep breath, held in the laugh, and told them they could face the camera away from them or even turn it off during "activities." But it was too late. I could tell by looking at the dad's face that he had already pictured the scene in his head and there was no way he was switching those monitors.

In an upcoming chapter, "Old Wives' Tales and Help from Grandma," I convey some of the wild and unusual remedies the elders swear by. But sometimes it's dads, and not grandmothers, who are the ones keeping up the old homeopathic techniques. However, I am not sure where this next dad learned this fix.

The visit was with a twelve-year-old girl who was there with a laceration on her arm. I was shocked to walk in and see a deep cut that was filthy and looked infected.

I asked the dad how long ago this cut occurred.

He answered, "Yesterdee." (Yes, that's how he said it). "We covered it in mud like you're supposed to, but it ain't gettin' no better."

I have gotten to the point in my career that nothing can shock me, so I replied, "I don't think you used enough mud."

He put his hand on his head and said, "Well, dang."

Don't worry. I then told him the correct way to treat a wound. I may love being sarcastic, but I am still a physician.

I do not want these anecdotes to seem as though I am disparaging dads, however, they do ask some very interesting questions. Once, I was seeing a couple with their newborn. I had just given them my spiel about the importance of keeping the baby away from other people so he wouldn't get sick.

Dad, who was a farmer, looked up and asked, "Would it be okay if he was around the livestock?"

Whenever things like this are asked, I have trained myself to pause while I figure out if I can laugh or if this is a real question. This time, no laughter came from dad, so I calmly told him that it would be safe.

A few minutes later, I was discussing breastfeeding with mom and dad interrupted. He announced that he would be able to help her with this. He explained that he worked on a dairy farm. This brought up some mental images that I quickly suppressed and will not share in this book.

Given that I am a dad, it would make sense that I should have no trouble communicating with them. However, sometimes I wish I had an interceptor. One afternoon, I was seeing a five-year-old for a well visit with her dad. I had never met him before, as the girl's mom had never missed a well appointment in the past. I asked why she wasn't at the visit.

Dad pointed up and kind of looked at me with a sad face. I thought, *oh my gosh, his wife has passed away.* I was very shocked and wasn't sure what to say.

When he saw the look on my face he said, "Oh no, she's just working upstairs and she wishes she was here."

Come to find out, she was working in the adult medical group located upstairs from my clinic. *Do they have dad interpreters?*

Another example of my incredible ability to communicate was during a visit with a dad and his three-month-old baby named Sam. Sam's father had brought him in to discuss reflux (spitting up). When I asked the dad about it, he said, "Oh, it's terrible."

He went on to explain that the baby spits up about every meal and in large amounts. I looked at the growth curve and the baby was in the

95th percentile. I said to dad, "Hey, you're really doing a great job of getting that back in because the baby is growing great."

He looked at me for a second and then he said, "Naw, we don't put it back in. We just clean it up."

And I started laughing and said, "No, I don't mean literally put it back in, I just mean you're feeding him enough to make him grow well."

He just stared blankly back at me. Obviously, he didn't understand what I was talking about.

Sometimes, the issues with communication fall more on the dad than me. While seeing a four-year-old for a cough, dad asked if I could help with the child's baby brother who was at home with a terrible diaper rash.

I asked the dad to describe the rash and he looked at me like I had asked him to explain nuclear physics. Trying to help him, I said, "Well, you know, if it looks like someone has taken a red pen and put dots all over the baby's diaper area then that's probably yeast. We can treat that with Nystatin."

And the dad looked at me and kind of shook his head and said, "No, we don't write on him."

To that I replied, "You can't come back without the baby's mother."

Grandparents are often the primary caregivers of many of my patients, and grandfathers can be just as funny as dads. I was taking care of a child who was three. In the past year, he had almost doubled in weight, which is not normal nor is it healthy. This child was so heavy he looked uncomfortable.

I was talking to his grandfather about my concerns and explaining the significant health issues this child could have if we didn't address his weight. I could tell Gramps wasn't buying it and so, finally he looked at me and said, "Doc, do you think the weight is just muscle? He's a really strong little guy. He can even hold a milk jug straight out without flinching!"

I started to laugh at his great joke until I saw the look on his face and realized he was serious. I poked my finger into the toddlers protruding belly and we all watched as the waves of fat cascaded away in all directions.

I replied, "No, I don't think it's *all* muscle."

WHO IS THE DAD?

GIVEN HOW MANY PATIENTS AN AVERAGE pediatrician sees in a day, it is impossible to remember every parent's name. Most of us adapt to this quickly by calling the patient's parents "Mom" and "Dad." When a female brings a child in, calling her mom will almost always be correct. As a side note, never call someone grandmother unless you are *sure* that they are the grandmother, no matter how old they look.

It's almost as bad as asking a non-pregnant woman when the baby is due. After making that mistake a few times early in my career, I made a rule to never ask a woman about pregnancy unless we are in the delivery room. Although not quite as cringeworthy, assuming that the male in the room with a patient is the dad leads to some embarrassing moments.

I had just such an instance early in my career when I was checking a newborn. I walked in to find a seventeen-year-old mom with an older man sitting beside her with a gray beard who reminded me of Willie Nelson.

"Willie" didn't say much during the visit, which is common for grandfathers. I have a lot of patients who are raised by single moms so I asked her, "Is the dad involved?"

Her face registered surprise and she said, "Yes! He is sitting right here!"

Willie Nelson's twin was the father! Unbelievably, I recovered quickly and asked, "But is he involved? Does he help with diapers and feeding?"

I think they bought it because I continued to see that baby until he was grown.

After that instance, I was much better at confirming that the male in the room was, indeed, the dad. Once, I was obtaining a family history and I asked, "Are you Dad?" to the guy who was there with the child.

He answered, "Well, I'm not the sperm donor, but I'm the dad."

Luckily, the child was a toddler and too young to understand. He had a bit of a low-collar way of saying it, but he did make his point.

The author Craig Lounsbrough said it more diplomatically when he penned, "The difference between a 'man' and a 'father' is that the former shares his genes, but the latter gives his life."

I had another situation with a sperm donor that turned into quite a puzzling case. Two moms brought their first baby in to see me for a newborn weight check. They named her Maria but told me they were thinking of changing the name.

"Why would you change her name?" I asked.

The mom who gave birth to her explained, "We picked a sperm donor out of a catalog. Because I am part Italian, we chose sperm from an Italian man."

I nodded, although I still did not understand.

She then opened the blanket and showed me Maria and asked, "Does she look Italian?"

I looked down at this very fair-skinned infant with bright red hair and rosy cheeks. "Well, not yet," I replied, trying to sound hopeful.

They were actually good sports about the whole thing, adding, "We figure the sperm donor had poor vision and checked the Italian box when he meant Irish."

Given how many years doctors go to school, it would seem we would be prepared for any situation. Nothing could be further from the truth. Unless I was absent on the day they discussed what to do when a father finds out he may not be related to his child.

One busy day at the clinic, I received a phone note from a concerned dad. He reported that his eighteen-year-old son had just given blood and they told him his blood type was A. Dad wanted to know what blood type his son was according to my records.

I wondered why my nurse didn't just look this up and tell him until I read further. Dad went on to say that this blood type was impossible since his blood type was B and the teen's mom's blood type was O.

Oops. Houston, we have a problem.

He was correct. His son's blood type should not be A with that combination of parents. I am not sure how he knew this, but it was probably from that pesky internet. Unfortunately, the blood type in my records was the same as the blood banks. I made up some vague answer about genetics being mysterious and sometimes unexpected things occur. I doubt he bought it and I am sure his wife had some explaining to do!

This is not the only time something like this has come up in my practice. A few times in my career, I have had couples with babies who presumably have the wrong color eyes. Occasionally, I will have a father question paternity because of the baby's eye color. I have the statistics memorized now so usually I have no trouble reassuring them. However, in the case of two blue-eyed parents with a brown-eyed baby it is a bit more difficult.

The way eye color is passed down, two blue-eyed parents should have a brown-eyed baby less than one percent of the time. In one of these cases, the dad asked me about it. I explained that although rare, it can happen. I felt pretty good about our discussion until he called the next week requesting paternity testing.

Speaking of eye color, I once had an awkward encounter with a mom when discussing this. The mom and her newborn baby had blue eyes and we were discussing the chances of the baby's eyes changing color. I asked mom what color dad's eyes were.

She thought about it and replied, "I am not sure."

I wasn't sure what to say. I wanted to ask, "You don't know the color of the baby's father's eyes or you don't know who the baby's father is?"

To this day, I wished I had asked, but I chickened out.

As you can imagine, the question of paternity can lead to some volatile situations. I was on call once in the hospital and they had to summon security to the labor and delivery area. There was a mom giving birth and while she was in labor, two of her male companions decided to get into a fight and had to be separated and escorted out of the hospital.

Once things calmed down, I went to check on the mom. I asked her, "What were they fighting about?"

She looked down and said, "Oh, we were fighting about the baby's name."

I looked at her sort of surprised and said, "That huge fight was about the name?"

And she said, "Yeah, that's what it was. We were fighting about the baby's name."

I didn't press her on it but I think we all know they were fighting about the baby's *last* name!

OLD WIVES' TALES AND HELP FROM GRANDMA

In the South, it is common for people to live in the same town as their parents and the town of Shelby, where I practice, is no exception. This allows many of my patients to stay with their grandparents during the day instead of being placed in daycare. This is wonderful for the parents because children get to stay home with family, plus they don't have to deal with the cost or the germs often associated with third-party facilities.

This also allows the local pediatrician to hear the plethora of old wives' tales that have been handed down for generations. Many of these lessons are true and helpful; others—not so much.

One of my most memorable experiences with a folklore remedy involved the treatment of thrush in a baby. Thrush is a very benign and common condition for newborns. It is a yeast infection that causes white plaques to build up in the baby's mouth. Newborns lack the oral defense system to prevent this infection and are prone to catching it.

The baby in question was April, a two-week-old female, who came in because her mom noticed something white in her mouth.

"It's not milk, because I can't wipe it off," she exclaimed.

I told her she was correct and told her the baby had thrush. I explained this infection to her and prescribed the baby oral Nystatin three times a day for a week.

The baby came back two weeks later for a well visit and I looked in the baby's mouth. The thrush was still there and now much worse.

I asked the mom, "Have you been using the medicine I prescribed?"

She answered, "I don't need to. My grandma told me a better way to get rid of the infection."

Part of me was afraid of the answer but I asked her what her grandmother suggested.

"We found a man who doesn't know his daddy and had him blow in the baby's mouth."

I know I should have asked how in the world this would help, but the first question that popped into my head was, "Why doesn't he know his daddy?"

She reported that his dad had died when he was very young.

She then went on to explain that it took a while to find such a man after posting the question on Facebook.

I instantly pictured the Facebook post:

After getting over my disgust at this mental image, I explained to her that this would not work.

I then gently explained I was going to call social services if she did not use the medicine that I had prescribed as the baby was definitely in pain at this point.

Luckily, she followed my instructions and the baby was better within a week. I'm sure the grandmother feels it was her technique that cured the baby.

Probably my favorite grandma trick is the treatment of swimmer's ear with urine. This technique has been around for a long time, but I often wonder who was the first to try it and—more importantly—why they tried it.

This old wives' tale really does work because the ammonia in urine kills the bacteria causing the infection. Many grandmas, however, say it must be baby urine (does baby urine have more ammonia?).

Whenever I see a patient with swimmer's ear, I often ask them if they know any babies with good aim.

Probably a couple of times each summer, patients come into the office with this condition who have unsuccessfully tried using urine in their ear before seeing me. If it's a boy, I often ask how they oriented their body so they could pee in their own ear.

Most look at me like I'm crazy and say, "I peed in a cup first and then put it in my ear, Dr. Benfield!"

Ha, as if I'm the dummy! I'm not the one with urine in my ear.

Speaking of putting urine in your ear, I once had a patient came in with swimmer's ear and I told her mom about the urine anecdote as a remedy.

Her eyes got big and she scolded me, "You have to be careful messing around with urine. When I was little, I had ringworm and my grandmother told me to put pee on it. I did and it turned into eczema!"

I nodded, as this was certainly an unexpected outcome. Inwardly, I knew that the rash was likely eczema all along as eczema often is mistaken for ringworm.

Probably the most common wives' tale I am asked about involves treating a baby with an umbilical hernia.

Before a baby is born, they receive their blood nutrients from mom through the vessels of the umbilical cord. This passes through an opening in their abdominal wall. After the umbilical cord is cut at delivery and later the remaining stump falls off, it takes some newborns a few months to seal up this opening. Sometimes, they are left with an umbilical hernia.

An umbilical hernia is not serious and is basically just a belly button that sticks out. In most cases, the hernia resolves before the child turns one.

I have found, however, that some grandmothers have an interesting technique to speed things along. This involves taping a silver dollar over the belly button. I was speechless the first time I pulled up a newborn's shirt and saw a large coin taped across their belly!

Whenever I see a newborn now with this hernia, I tell them it is not necessary to use a silver dollar. Most seem relieved and will say, "My grandma said we should try that!"

I was once explaining this to a mom and told her, "The silver dollar trick does work ninety-eight percent of the time, but doing nothing also works ninety-eight percent of the time."

The mom replied, "Do you think a quarter would work better?"

Sometimes I am too clever for my own good.

One of the more unusual stories I heard when I first moved to Shelby was about "hiving."

I was seeing a newborn and the mom asked, "Can I give the baby catnip tea?"

After getting over my shock, I asked why she would want to do such a thing.

"Because he keeps hiving. My great-grandmother says the tea will help."

"What in the world is hiving?" I asked.

She explained this is when the baby is asleep and his eyes move around under his eyelids and sometimes makes odd facial gestures. She went on to say that this is very bad but no one had explained to her why.

I knew this was simply REM sleep and tried to explain this to the mom. I told her catnip tea was a sedative (which is why it makes the hiving go away since it puts the baby in a deeper sleep phase) and should never be given to a baby.

She replied that she understood but great-grandma would not be happy.

Luckily, this myth seems to have stopped being passed down. I have not been asked about it in years.

What impresses me about old wives' tales is how many exist. I have been practicing for nearly thirty years and I continue to hear both familiar and new ones that amaze me.

One morning while doing a well visit, a mom told me, "I have a four-month-old and her grandmother doesn't want her to put weight on her legs because it will cause her to be bowlegged."

This is one of the most common myths I hear and I assured her it was not true.

The mom then surprised me by adding, "Well, what about tickling?"

I asked her what about it?

She answered, "Well, when I tickle the baby, my grandmother gets upset. She told me if you tickle a baby this young it will make them stutter later in life."

That was a new one! I felt very comfortable telling her there was no truth to that and she had my permission to tickle the baby.

The mom was so happy and I knew I just went up a notch in her eyes, but most certainly down a few in grandma's.

This next mom had been told a similar odd tale by her grandmother. She came in with her eighteen-month-old son for a checkup.

She was very concerned about the way he slept. When I asked her what the issue was, she said, "Well, he sleeps on his belly and he tucks his knees up underneath him."

I explained to her this was a very common and safe way to sleep.

She replied, "Should I stop feeding him sweets?"

I thought this was a quick change of subject, but started to explain that sweets were not the best for his teeth or his health but an occasional one would do no harm.

She interrupted me with, "No. My grandma says the more sweets the child eats the more he will sleep with his knees up underneath him."

I was distracted with the thought that I had a bag of M&M's at home that I could try this experiment with tonight. But I managed to compose myself and reassure her it had nothing to do with sweets but rather the way the child likes to sleep.

Some grandmother tricks work quite well. I once had a grandmother tell me she had nine grandchildren and none of them had ever had to seek medical care for a diaper rash because of her special diaper cream.

I asked her how she made it while picturing us making millions by patenting this miracle cream.

She explained that she takes regular flour, lights it on fire, and burns it. *The millions of dollars went "poof" in my mind.*

I was looking confused and she explained, "You burn it in a frying pan and then put it on the baby's bottom and it will cure all diaper rash."

Captain Obvious (me) replied, "You cool it down first, right?"

She looked at me like I'm an idiot and said, "Of course!"

Unfortunately, some of the lessons that are passed down about raising children not only don't work, but can cause harm.

Early in my career, I was called to the emergency room to see a ten-year-old with a swollen foot. The child's name was Tim. When I walked in the room, I could tell he was in a great deal of pain.

"What happened to your foot?" I asked.

Tim replied, "Well, five days ago I was walking in the woods and stepped on a 'coon trap." (For those of you who don't know, that's a raccoon trap.)

He went on to say, "It snapped over my foot, and the steel jaw went into the top and bottom of my foot."

I remember thinking that must have been terribly painful. I asked, "What did you do then?" expecting him to say he went to the emergency room.

Then his dad chimed in. "We took him over to his grannie's and she put some fatback on it."

I am sure my look said it all.

He continued, "His granny knows about stuff like that and she wrapped the fatback around his foot and covered that with cabbage leaves."

I continued staring at him in shock and repeated, "cabbage leaves."

He looked down bashfully and replied, "I know you are supposed to use tobacco leaves, but we didn't have any."

I knew I had put it off long enough and slowly pulled back the coverings to reveal his foot. I expected it to be bad, but it was much worse. It was swollen two times the normal size of a foot with angry, red puncture wounds on top and below, each one draining foul-smelling pus.

The dad saw my face and said, "I sure do wish we could have found some tobacco leaves."

My first thought was, *I wish you had brought him to the doctor when this first happened.* Luckily, I kept that to myself and promptly admitted him to the hospital for IV antibiotics.

Tim had to stay in the hospital for two weeks and ended up needing to have a surgeon drain the awful-looking wounds.

This next mom would have been better off not listening to her grandmother as well. The mom came in with her coughing three-month-old baby.

When I examined her, I heard wheezing and explained to the mom that the baby had a condition called bronchiolitis, a viral infection that can make babies wheeze and have trouble breathing.

She told me it had been going on for six days. Because the baby was so sick, I asked why she waited so long to bring the baby in to be checked.

"Well, my grandmother told me that turpentine would fix it."

"You gave the baby turpentine!?" I said, alarmed.

She gave me the "what, are you stupid?" look that I seem to attract. She explained, "Oh no. We soaked a rag in it and put it next to the baby's crib."

"And that helps the baby breathe?" I asked incredulously.

"Yep," she replied with the confidence of a medical school professor.

I understand how some old wives' tales get handed down because before we had pediatricians and virtual visits, a grandmother was the person parents most often turned to for advice about their children. I do not, however, understand how this next bit of advice originated.

The baby's name was Samuel. He was a pudgy three-month-old boy who was in my office for a checkup. This was the mom's first child and so I was putting special emphasis on safety.

"Now, it's time to start being careful about the child rolling. Sometimes, the first time a baby rolls, it is right off a bed."

Samuel's mom looked at me sheepishly, so I asked, "Oh, has your child already rolled off a bed?"

She replied, "No." She then looked down and said, "I better not say."

I encouraged her to tell me what was on her mind. She went on, "Well, my grandmother said that there's an old wives' tale that she says is true. She told me if a baby doesn't roll off a bed or a couch by the time it's one, it will die."

Her grandmother, according to her, had let all three of her children roll off the bed to prevent this.

I promised her that this was not true. She seemed to feel better when I explained to her that ninety-nine percent of people never roll off a bed in their life and somehow manage to live.

In general, I think most moms benefit from the expertise of their mothers and grandmothers. The examples above are, albeit funny, not common occurrences. These just stick in my mind more easily than when good advice is passed down. Just don't let the baby roll off the bed!

MOMMY WORRIES

Having a new baby is one of the most anxiety provoking times in a person's life. This seems to hit women particularly hard. I have known women who before having children were perfectly calm and relaxed, yet turned into nervous wrecks as parents. I don't think people without children realize the huge responsibility that people feel once they have a child.

I've often had moms report that they're not sleeping well after having a new baby, but not for the reason you would think. It's not because they get up for nighttime feedings, but rather it's because they sit and stare at the baby through much of the night. They are afraid if they go to sleep something will happen to the infant. This thought is perfectly understandable.

One of the key skills in being a good pediatrician is managing this anxiety. It is important to relieve the mom's worries without sounding too condescending or making the mom feel like she is being silly.

There are times, however, when the mom's worries are so outlandish that this can be a difficult task. For example, one summer morning, I was discussing a fifteen-month-old baby's eating habits with her mom. The mom was very worried that the baby was not eating enough. I explained to her that toddlers often have very unpredictable eating habits and that her baby was growing quite well.

She seemed very relieved and then admitted, "I was worried that she had anorexia."

I chuckled a bit until I realized she was serious. I quickly composed myself and with a very serious tone reassured her that this was not the case. For the rest of the day, I had a mental image of a toddler in a diaper standing in front of a mirror thinking, "Do I look fat?"

Recently, psychologists have come up with a new term for moms who are deeply involved in every aspect of their children's lives. They call this parenting style being a "helicopter mom" and all pediatricians are very familiar with this behavior.

One of my favorite examples of this type of mom occurred during a visit with a seventeen-year-old named Davis. I had just diagnosed Davis with a sinus infection and noticed he was allergic to amoxicillin. Knowing that he would be going to college soon, I decided to use this as a teaching moment.

I looked at his mom and said, "Don't answer this question. This is for your son to answer."

I then turned to Davis and said, "I am going to give you amoxicillin to treat this infection. Is that okay?"

Before I had even finished speaking the mom blurted out, "No! Don't give him amoxicillin. He is allergic to it!"

I told the mom I was trying to teach her son that and she was not supposed to answer.

She apologized and said, "As soon as I heard the word amoxicillin, I freaked out!"

A funny sidebar to this story is I had almost the same situation a few months later with another seventeen-year-old male who was allergic to amoxicillin. I told the mom the story above and we had a good laugh.

She then looked up and said, "Wait, are you saying my son is allergic to amoxicillin?"

Two very different moms.

I do not want to give the impression that being a "helicopter mom" is a bad thing. In fact, I would much rather a parent use this style than to be uninvolved in their child's life.

However, I will admit that sometimes these parents can make a visit challenging, as was the case with a cute toddler named Elliot.

Elliot's parents are very high-functioning professionals who I am sure are nice people, but honestly, it can be hard to be their pediatrician. Each visit with them is spent analyzing every detail of Elliot's life and our visits are so long I have to book their appointments in double slots.

One memorable visit was at Elliot's eighteen-month well check. When I asked about developmental milestones the mom pulled out a two-page printout of every milestone. It was broken down into social, verbal, gross motor, and fine motor development. Instead of just allowing me to read it, the mom read through each section looking up often to gauge my response.

I nodded and praised Elliot with each new accomplishment she read but had to hold in my laughter when she described one of his most recent milestones. She reported that her precocious eighteen-month-old knew his ABC's up to C. C? Was that really worthy of listing as a skill?

I have found that there are two types of anxious moms. The first type is very open about their worries and will say things like, "I know this is crazy, but I am so worried that his headaches are being caused by a brain tumor."

I love these types of moms and find them easy to work with. Knowing what they are worried about is helpful in reassuring them without sounding condescending.

The second type of anxious mom will often give me a distrusting stare and ask questions like, "Are you sure?" or "Don't you think we should get some labs?"

This requires patience and tact to try to figure out what the mom is actually worried about. When I meet a new mom, I often encourage her to use the first approach and always ask me about what specifically they are worried about.

At times, their worries are about very rare conditions. In these cases, I reassure them with a lesson I learned in medical school: "When you hear hoof beats, think horses, not zebras." In other words, when faced with a medical problem, the diagnosis is more likely to be something common than rare.

I had a mom ask me once if I thought her son had a rare medical condition and I told her the above phrase.

She responded with, "We don't have any horses. But we do have goats!"

This was not the only time that one of my attempts to explain something with an analogy fell flat. I was seeing a young teen male with chronic back pain and I told his mom that I was going to refer him to a physical therapist.

She asked, "What about a chiropractor?"

I then told her that the decision to go to a physical therapist versus a chiropractor was one of personal preference. She didn't seem to understand so I said, "It's like in the movie *Twilight* (which was very popular at this time); some people are team vampire and some people are team werewolf."

She smiled and said, "I am team werewolf."

I was inwardly proud of my excellent analogy until she followed up with, "So, is the werewolf the physical therapist or the chiropractor?"

The following mom was great in that she told me exactly what she was worried about but in an interesting way. She arrived at the clinic with her two-year-old and my nurse said she seemed a bit upset.

I walked in the exam room and, before I could speak, she pulled up the child's shirt and said, "I need you to check my baby's skin."

I told her I would be happy to check her baby and asked what was going on.

She hurriedly replied, "Look at these bumps. The daycare said it was a rash! Do you think this is a rash? I want you to look at it and tell me if it is a rash."

So, I sort of laughed and told her, "Yes, it's a rash, but do you want to know what to do about the rash?"

She put her hand on her forehead and asked me again to be sure, "So, it is a rash?"

I explained to her that a rash is simply any change in the skin and that this was likely from something that irritated her child's skin. I then told her that this was nothing to be concerned about and the rash would quickly go away after she applied some mild steroid cream.

She did not seem reassured. As she left, I heard her mutter, "I can't believe she has a rash."

I occasionally teach medical students in my office and when I ask them if they are interested in becoming a pediatrician, the answer I often hear is, "I like kids, but I don't think I could deal with the worrying moms."

I reassure them by explaining that all parents worry about their children, but most handle it well and are not difficult. I had just finished explaining this to one of my students when we went into a room that contradicted that sentiment.

The baby's name was Libby and she was the newborn of a first-time mom. As soon as we walked in, I could tell the mom was very flustered.

Many anxious moms do not wait for you to introduce yourself and in perfect form she started with, "Thank goodness you are here. I think my baby has an infected belly button."

My approach to moms like this is to relieve their concerns right away so I washed my hands and went straight to check the baby. When I pulled up Libby's shirt, I noticed that the umbilical cord stump was still present as expected, but it was covered in a white paste and smelled horrible.

I asked the mom, "What is this all over the belly button?"

"That's peroxide and baby powder. I put it on there because I was so worried it would get infected."

I explained to her we do not put anything on the belly button except for occasionally rubbing alcohol.

She said the nurses at the hospital told her this but she couldn't sleep thinking about how gross it looked and she knew it had to be covered in bacteria.

After cleaning the area with alcohol, I reminded her that the umbilical stump falling off was a normal process and not to put anything else on it.

She nodded and replied, "Can you write that down for me?"

I was confused and asked her, "What do you mean, write what down?"

"Will you write on a piece of paper not to put anything on the belly button. I am so frazzled I am afraid I will forget and still put something on it."

After the visit, my medical student said, "I am not sure pediatrics is right for me."

I reassured him that this was an unusual visit and was the first time I had ever written someone a note reminding them NOT to do something.

Parents are not the only ones who worry. Grandparents are often even more anxious about their grandchildren. The biggest worry of grandparents? Unquestionably, diabetes. I answer more questions about this condition than almost every other condition combined.

During the summer, kids seem to drink a lot more because it is so hot and, of course, they urinate a lot more as well. Because of this, I average one visit per month of what we call "check for diabetes" visits.

It usually starts with me walking in and before I can say hello they say, "I need his sugar checked. He is peeing all the time."

Checking the child for diabetes is easy and only involves getting a urine specimen. I have done this hundreds of times and only twice did the child have diabetes. When the test is negative, these are fun visits. The grandmother leaves happy and the child is relieved that they don't have to take any shots.

A four-year-old girl came in one time to see me because she was having some burning with urination. Her urine was clear and I said to the mom, "There is no evidence of an infection. And you can tell her grandma that she doesn't have diabetes."

Her face lit up and she said, “I wasn’t going to say anything, but my mom is always telling me I need to have her checked. She will be so relieved.”

For many moms, bringing their newborn baby to the doctor is obviously a nerve-racking experience. I notice this most with younger moms so I do my best to explain everything and put them at ease. I once had a memorable experience with a mom who, because of her nervousness, was obviously not thinking clearly.

The mom was nineteen and had brought her two-month-old in with cold symptoms. After I listened to his heart and lungs I said, “Put him on your shoulder, I’m going to check his ears.”

I turned away for a second to pick up my otoscope and when I turned back, she had her baby on top of both shoulders with his legs along each side of her neck. It was a hilarious image. He had a big smile on his face and because he did not have good head control, he was swaying his head back and forth, which reminded me of Stevie Wonder.

She had both hands behind her head holding the baby and he had both his hands intertwined in her hair.

My face must have shown my shock because at that point she realized, “Oh my gosh! You mean just up against my shoulder!”

She was mortified and I told her not to worry; that this happened all the time. *It was the first.*

Often, some of the funniest moments I have are with patients who have never seen me before. They think I’m a typical doctor and they don’t expect my sense of humor, which can lead to some awkward moments.

This next young mom I was seeing brought her first baby in for his initial newborn well check. After asking questions about her delivery and the baby's time in the newborn nursery, I stood up to examine him. As I reached around my neck to grab my stethoscope, I realized I had left it at my desk.

I smiled at my mistake and jokingly said, "You trust me with the health of your baby and I don't even have a stethoscope."

The mom looked at me very anxiously and said, "I didn't know you didn't have a stethoscope when I made the appointment!"

This dear mom was so anxious that she assumed that somehow this was her fault. I quickly reassured her that I did own a stethoscope, it was just at my desk.

BLESS HER HEART

For those of you who do not live in the South, when someone says, "Bless your heart," it translates to: "You poor thing, I'm so sorry that happened to you!" or "That's terrible. I hope things get better for you."

But when someone says, "Bless *HER* heart," it is an attempt to be polite while thinking, "She did something she shouldn't have, but is not smart enough to know better."

Here's an example. "She wrote her PIN number on her debit card? *Well, bless her heart.*"

In my clinic, I am often faced with moments where I think of this phrase but, of course, do not verbalize it. This chapter is full of "bless her heart" moments. Don't worry, I have an entire chapter of my own "bless his heart" moments in a later chapter, "My Foot in My Mouth."

As in any town or city, here in Shelby, you come across some folks who are "salt of the Earth" parents. This chapter goes out to those who made me smile with their no-nonsense approach to life. They remind me why I chose to practice in a small town.

Some of the "bless her heart" parents have made me laugh even when they didn't know they were being funny.

Halfway through a well visit for a three-month-old boy named Tanner, his mom told me she had some questions about feeding him cereal. First, you're not supposed to feed a three-month-old baby cereal. You're supposed to wait until at least four months, but that wasn't the point. She wanted to know what she could use to wash down the cereal after the baby ate it.

"Can I give him juice or water or formula?" she asked me. She added that the cereal was so flaky that Tanner was having trouble getting it down.

I didn't understand why the cereal was so flaky, so, I asked, "Are you adding formula to the cereal?"

She said, "Oh! I didn't know I was supposed to."

She was feeding the baby dry cereal flakes! Anything this baby eats for the rest of his life will seem so delicious compared to the dry mess that was his first introduction to food.

On a Friday afternoon, my last patient of the day was a mom with her three-year-old daughter, Lulu, whose real name is Lucy. They came in for a rash that mom said were flea bites.

Her first sentence was, "It is not my fault that she has flea bites. I was trying to keep the cat from killing her kittens."

A rash is usually a quick visit, but the impending weekend could wait. So, I sat down and waited for what I knew would be an interesting story. Mom went on to tell me the reason Lulu had the flea bites was because she had to bring the kittens into the house to protect them from their mother. I nodded as if this were obvious and asked her to continue.

She reported that she figured out this murder plot two days prior when she was in her car and was getting ready to back out of her driveway. She looked back, and the mom and the kittens were right behind the car, underneath the wheel.

Her exact words were, "She put them durn kittens there to try and kill them! So, I had to bring them inside to protect them."

I wanted to say (but did not) that I hoped there weren't any guns in the house, because this cat sounded smart and who knows? She might try to shoot her kittens!

Sometimes, funny moments occur because of my inability to explain things clearly. After working in Cleveland County for many years, I have learned to explain medical issues in simple terms. However, this was not the case when I first started practicing.

Early in my career, I was seeing an eight-year-old male named Jonathon who had come in with his mom to discuss constipation. He was having a terrible time trying to use the bathroom, so I explained to mom in great detail how important it was for him to stool every day. I went on to tell her that Jonathon really needed to "get some good bowel habits."

The next day, mom called and talked to my nurse, explaining that she had sent her husband out to two different pharmacies and he couldn't find any "bowel habits" anywhere!

My nurse had no idea what she was talking about, but when she relayed this to me, I understood immediately. And that was the last time I used *that* term.

As I spent more time with families, when it came to this topic, I learned to say, "We need to make sure he goes poop every day."

This story likely caused me to blush a bit at the time. I was seeing a one-week-old baby for a well visit and mom asked me about the baby's rash. She said he had a small bump on his lip and one on his penis and she seemed very concerned about it. I explained it was a typical newborn rash and nothing to be worried about.

She asked, "So, you don't think it is herpes?"

I told her no, that the rash was not consistent with that condition.

She replied, "Because herpes runs in our family."

I wanted to tell her that herpes is an infection and doesn't run in families. Then again, maybe her family reunions were different than mine.

I am listed as the primary doctor for more than 2,000 children in our area, so remembering everyone's names is not possible. I am good, however, at remembering faces. Which led to my confusion when I was seeing Joel, who was in the hospital for dehydration.

It had been a year since I had seen Joel, and I remembered him, but I did not recognize the lady with him in the room. I awkwardly asked, "Now, forgive me for asking, but you are mom, aren't you?"

She looked at me like I was crazy and said, "Yeah, I'm mom."

I replied, "I am sorry for not recognizing you. It has been a while since I have seen you." In my mind, I was thinking, *I have never seen this lady in my life.*

Then her eyes lit up, "Oh, I have had a haircut!"

I pretended to be convinced, commenting, "Yes, that must be it."

After I finished seeing Joel and was preparing to leave, I said, "It was great to see you again, even though with your new hairstyle I didn't recognize you."

She looked as if she suddenly remembered something and replied, "Oh yeah, well, I also lost eighty-five pounds."

I couldn't help but laugh and said, "Maybe *that* is why I didn't recognize you."

She smiled sheepishly and replied, "That may be it."

In my town, some children don't go to the dentist as often as they should, so it falls to the pediatrician to help look after the children's teeth. One of my most memorable teeth encounters was with a three-year-old named Tina. Even at this young age, Tina already had significant plaque and I asked mom if she had taken her to see a dentist.

She replied, "No, not yet, but, you know, dental problems run in the family. Her daddy's got bad teeth and both her sisters do, too."

I couldn't help but notice as she was explaining this that she had some of the worst teeth I had ever seen. There was a lot of brown decay and a few of her front teeth had been chipped off.

I don't know if she noticed me looking at her, but she added, "I've got bad teeth, too, but mine came from a car accident."

I just nodded in agreement. But, inside, I was wondering if she got hit by the plaque truck … or what kind of accident could give you bad teeth like that. I made her promise she would take Tina and her sisters to the dentist.

One of a doctor's least favorite aspects of the job is being on call. Thankfully, we have a call service where a nurse takes the initial call and gives the patient advice. They have protocols to handle most situations and only call the physician if the child sounds significantly ill or if they cannot handle the question. So, when my phone rings, I know it is either something serious or something odd.

I received a call one Sunday night from a nurse whose first sentence was, "I am sorry to bother you, but I don't know what to do with this one."

She explained that a mom was calling regarding the behavior of her three-year-old son. I was beginning to wonder why this necessitated a late-night phone call when she said, "Mom says she is afraid for her life."

I was not expecting that response and asked my nurse, "How old did you say this child is?"

"Three," she told me. "But mom says he is being very aggressive and she is afraid of him."

I certainly felt bad that this mom was having to deal with an aggressive child. But is she really afraid of a twenty-four-pound three-year-old? I had a brief image of the Chucky doll from the *Child's Play* horror movies, but recovered and told the nurse, "I think they will be fine tonight. I am happy to discuss this with them tomorrow in the clinic."

When I saw them on Monday, I would love to tell you that the mom was right and this child was indeed scary. However, he was just a typical toddler who was having tantrums.

Everyone knows that when a woman is pregnant, she will often develop strange food cravings. On television, the craving is usually pickles or ice cream in the middle of the night. However, pediatricians know that a common, but not well known, craving is cornstarch. I am not sure what the scientific basis is for this, but it is something I would commonly see when I worked in the hospital.

I was attending a delivery once and the obstetrician put the baby on mom's chest right after it was born. Newborns often come out with a white, paste-like substance covering their body. This particular baby had so much of it that it looked like wet paint.

The mom took one look at her baby and exclaimed, "Oh no! I knew I shouldn't have eaten all that cornstarch when I was pregnant. My mother warned me this would happen!"

Many times, I come home and tell my wife about the funny things that happened in my office that day and she will shake her head and ask, "Did that really happen?"

My response is always the same, "I can't make this stuff up."

One case of "life is stranger than fiction" occurred on a Wednesday morning when I had a two-week-old baby come in for a checkup. The mom was only seventeen so her parents had come to the visit as well.

My nurse had told me before I went in the room, "Speak slowly, they are a bit simple." Before I could even introduce myself, the grandmother said, "I want to show you what I pulled off the baby."

Being that this was a newborn, I could not imagine what she had pulled off. My mind was spinning as she began rummaging through her purse and finally pulled out a medicine bottle. I leaned in close and I could see there was something green at the bottom of the bottle. *What in the world is green on a baby?*

She then removed the lid and reached in, pulled the green item out and handed it to me. *Should I put on a glove? Should I run out of the room screaming?* My brain said no, but my hand reached out to take hold of the spectacle. With dread, I looked at my hand to find a tiny green tick.

I now said my first sentence since walking into the room: "It's a tick."

Grandma looked at me like I was an idiot and replied, "Yes, it is a tick. I pulled it off the baby's head."

I then asked the obvious question, "Why is it green?"

"Scope," was her only answer.

I had no words, so I just looked at each of them with a confused look on my face.

The mom then sighed, as if she wished she had chosen a different doctor, and said, "We didn't have any rubbing alcohol, so we used Scope."

As I handed the minty-fresh tick back to Grandma I thought, *I can't make this stuff up.*

INNER LAUGHTER

THERE ARE MANY TRAITS THAT GO along with being a good pediatrician. It is important to be a good listener, compassionate, knowledgeable, and patient. However, I think an undervalued skill is the ability to maintain a professional demeanor no matter what the situation. It took me years to develop what I call my "Inner Laughter." This is the ability to nod with a straight face even though inside I am hysterically laughing.

Early in my career, I had not developed my poker face and would often accidently laugh out loud at these verbal miscues. Now, as a seasoned pediatrician, I can act seriously whenever I hear something that's not meant as a joke but impulsively makes me want to crack-up.

What follows are perfect examples of parents who put this special ability to the test.

A mom of a nine-year-old child called and said dramatically, "You just don't understand, Dr. Benfield. Her belly is just killing her! She says it has never hurt this bad. I don't know what I'm going to do."

I tried to calm her down a bit and then started going through some questions to try and figure out what was causing her pain.

Mom interrupted me and said, "She's nine. You don't think she's going through her menopause already, do you?"

Even though I knew she meant menstrual cycle, I did not correct her. I didn't know what was causing her daughter's belly pain, but I was sure it wasn't menopause.

It is interesting to me how one word can change an entire impression of a visit. I was seeing a six-month-old baby for a well visit and I asked the mom about the boy's temperament.

She replied, "He's a good baby. He only cries when he is in his cage."

I looked at her with one eyebrow raised (well, in my mental image of myself it was raised; I never have been able to raise only one eyebrow) and she quickly corrected herself and blurted out, "I mean the crib!"

She was very embarrassed and was truly afraid that I was going to call social services. She was a great mom and I reassured her that I knew what she meant.

"What's going on with your son today?" I asked the dad of a two-month-old boy.

He answered, "Well, he's coughing and snuffling and he seems to have a lot of 'ingestion' in his nose."

A mom came in with her three-year-old son because she was concerned about his speech. When I asked her to describe the problem she said, "Well, we can't understand him well. He can't 'punctuate' his words right."

I wanted to tell her that punctuation was difficult and that I still didn't know how to properly use a semicolon.

A mom and I were discussing her child's cold symptoms. She told me, "Well, he has already seen a doctor on one of those 'telepathic' visits, but he is no better."

I just nodded and didn't tell her that those visits are called virtual or telehealth visits. However, I did like the image of myself sitting with my eyes closed and my palms up, seeing the patient with only my mind. Maybe someday.

I was seeing a two-month-old baby with his grandmother who wanted to discuss the baby's problem with spitting up. The grandmother reported this was a horrible problem and explained, "We feed this baby and he just 'ejaculates' it up all over us!"

I chuckled awkwardly for a second but she just kept talking. I don't think she knew what she said and I certainly wasn't going to tell her.

A family came in with their child who was experiencing some type of cold symptoms. The mother insisted on giving her antibiotics, telling me, "I'm just really worried about her." She went on, "Grandma was just in the hospital and died and came back."

"What?" I asked, wondering if I heard her right.

"Yeah, she died and came back. So, they gave her some antibiotics and now she's doing better."

With a slight grin, I nodded and said, "Oh, okay."

"She had a sinus infection of the lungs," the mother told me with authority.

At a well visit for a child with his arm in a cast, I asked him, "What happened to your arm?"

Mom answered, saying, "Well, you know, we live in Lincoln County. Those ER doctors in Lincoln County don't know nothing. So, we went there on Monday and they took x-rays and they said he had a fracture of his arm."

"I see," I answered, not wanting to disparage my ER colleagues.

She went on, "But then, we went to an orthopedist and they said it was broken."

I was seeing an eight-year-old boy for the first time. As a new patient, I took his history and asked if he had been circumcised.

His mom's eyes got very wide and she exclaimed, "Lord no! I want to be a grandma someday."

It took me a second to catch on. But then I smiled and said, "Not castrated, circumcised." I went on to explain to her what that meant.

"Oh, yeah," she said matter-of-factly, "he had that done shortly after birth."

A mom was telling me that her baby had kept her up last night and she had an interesting way of describing it. "I tell you what, that baby kept me up 24/7 last night. I was up 24/7!"

I bet none of you have ever stayed up that long.

I had a dad tell me once, "We give the baby that Enfamil breast milk." I am not sure where they bought that.

I asked the mom of a new patient if he had ever been hospitalized.

She replied, “No, but once he went to the emergency room and they ‘glanced’ a boil.”

It took all of my will not to add, “Good thing they saw it out of the corner of their eye.” Instead, I just released the inner laughter.

got milk?

BREASTFEEDING

I KNOW WHAT YOU ARE THINKING. *Is this a proper subject for a lighthearted book?* To me, breastfeeding is simply another way of helping my patients grow and thrive. Before I became a physician, I had no idea how difficult breastfeeding can be for a first-time mom. One would think babies would have an instinct on how to do this, but believe me, they do not.

Most newborns have little idea about how to do this correctly and would rather sleep than eat. Therefore, my visits with new breastfeeding moms are crucial to teach the mom how to feed the baby correctly to avoid dehydration. I see breastfed newborns more frequently than formula-fed ones during the first month to make sure the babies are gaining weight. It is during these visits that some of my funniest situations have occurred.

One of my favorites of these stories happened when I was seeing two new parents for a weight check with their newborn. I explained to the mom that, at this stage, the baby needed lots of milk. Because of this, I told her to feed the infant from both breasts each feeding.

She looked at me very confused and said, "I don't think I can get both nipples in the baby's mouth at the same time!"

I tried not to laugh and looked at her husband to see if he thought this was as funny as I did. No such luck; he was staring at me with a very confused look on his face. I explained to them that I meant each feeding should consist of the baby eating from one breast and then the other.

They were both relieved and felt they could manage this much easier than what they thought I had meant. I saw these folks twice a week for the first couple of months as they required just a bit more hand holding than most.

On another occasion, it was my turn to be confused by the way a mom was breastfeeding. I had seen a ten-day-old newborn one week earlier for her first visit and she was not nursing well. I referred the family to a lactation specialist and was now happily surprised at this visit to see that the baby's weight had improved significantly.

I praised the mom and asked what she was doing differently.

She explained that after their visit with lactation, they were now doing "triple feeds."

I quickly did the math and then turned to dad with a confused look on my face.

He quickly put both hands over his chest and said, "Oh, no, not me!"

The mom then rescued me by explaining that the "third" feed was breast milk in a bottle.

Often, when writing down these events, I leave out details that are unrelated to the story, however in this case, I feel a mental image is important. I was seeing a two-month-old baby and the mom asked me who was going to be giving him his shots. I told her that Margaret was the nurse that was giving shots on that day.

She replied, "Great, I am glad she is a female as I want to breastfeed while the baby gets his shots and I don't feel comfortable breastfeeding in front of a man."

Now, let me describe mom. She was a large lady, wearing a small tube top which she was literally spilling out of. She didn't feel comfortable breastfeeding in front of a man but her top left literally nothing to the imagination.

When I went back to the vaccination room, Margaret had gone to lunch and a new nurse was covering for her. I gave her the chart and told her about mom's request. It was this nurse's second day working in my clinic and she said she didn't feel comfortable with mom feeding during shots.

I told her just to let mom know and I was sure it would be fine. So, after telling the mom this, the nurse had the baby on the examining table and was getting ready to give the injections. She reported that the mom then pulled down her tube top and standing over the baby lowered the breast into the baby's mouth.

As I stated earlier, this was a rather large lady and my nurse said all she could see was the baby's hands and feet. This gave me a mental image of the wicked witch trapped under the house in *The Wizard of Oz*.

The nurse wasn't sure what to do as this mom was breastfeeding the baby upside down and waiting for her to continue. She gently moved the mom's breast aside and gave the baby the first shot in his thigh. The baby screamed and the mom pushed her breast farther into the baby's mouth. The nurse could hear the baby choking as its hands and feet were moving wildly back and forth. She pulled the mom up to see a blue baby gasping for air with milk running out the side of his mouth. Once the baby recovered, mom agreed it would be best to do the rest of the shots without her laying on top of him.

Later, the nurse came to see me and said this would be her last day as this job was way too stressful. I explained this was the first time anything like this had happened and managed to talk her into staying.

When it comes to breastfeeding, dads are rarely very helpful. We want to help but the closest we get to having any knowledge on the subject is when we are holding the baby and it turns its head looking for our "breasts." Not only does this make us very uncomfortable, it really doesn't make us experts.

I did have one dad, however, who felt he had some inside information on nursing. He was a dairy farmer and very proudly explained to me (complete with hand gestures) how he got his wife's milk to come down prior to the baby feeding.

Feeling a bit embarrassed by his explanation, I looked to his wife for help. She was mortified and looked like she wanted to hide under the exam table. Dad continued smiling like he had cured cancer as I changed the subject.

Breastfeeding a baby is naturally the mom's responsibility, so when I discuss this issue with parents, I find myself talking to the mom more than the dad. This does not stop some new fathers from trying to give me their opinion on how things are going.

One dad started explaining to me the troubles the baby was having by reporting, "One side is not producing milk as well as the other. So, the baby has been feeding from the good side most of the time."

I replied, "It is important to feed from both sides and the more the baby feeds, the more milk that breast will produce."

Dad countered before mom could answer with, "The baby really doesn't like the bad breast. I am not sure we can get him to latch on to it."

I reassured them that they should start with that side each feeding and that the baby would adapt.

The dad then turned to his wife and said, "Okay, honey. We are going to have to start with the bad breast each feeding," as though he had to translate what I was saying.

The mom, however, had reached her breaking point. She loudly exclaimed, "Can we stop calling it the bad breast!"

There must be a gene that makes fathers enjoy telling "dad jokes" all the time. I have the added advantage of telling "medical dad jokes" which never fails to amuse me more than others within earshot. On one occasion, I actually came up with my own joke and invented a new word at the same time.

I was seeing a new mom and asked her if the newborn was breastfeeding well from both breasts. As mentioned in the story above, newborns commonly have trouble nursing with one side.

She replied, "Yes, he is doing great. He goes to either side without issue."

As soon as she said this, my brain instantly invented the new term! "Oh, so your baby is ambibreastious!"

The mom laughed and did not believe me when I told her I had just coined the word on the spot. My partners, on the other hand, were not impressed when I went bragging about it. They told me to concentrate more on seeing patients and less on entertaining myself.

Ha! I will show them when this new term is in the next Webster's dictionary!

I will admit that there is a lot of societal pressure on new moms to breastfeed. I try to make sure every new mom understands that this is a personal choice and that the baby will still be healthy if the mom chooses to use formula.

I had one mom with an interesting take on breastfeeding. She was an upper middle-class lady from upstate New York who has always been one of my harder parents to interact with. She tended to be a bit grumpy and never seemed to enjoy the role of motherhood. I had taken care of her first child and she was in to see me at the initial well check for her second baby.

I was very upbeat and bubbly and asked her how things were going.

She said, "Well, it's going fine," and just kind of shrugged her shoulders.

Trying to make her proud of how things were going, I bragged on the baby's weight gain and how healthy he looked. I then made the comment that breastfeeding must be going very well.

She said, "Well, to tell you the truth, breastfeeding is just going fine. It's easy. The baby seems to like it. But personally, I think it's unnatural."

That caught me a bit off guard. But I let her go on.

She said, "I don't like doing it. I think it's gross and I am only doing it because I know the health benefits."

Unnatural? I couldn't think of anything more natural but I wisely held my tongue.

When I see a mom who is still breastfeeding at the one-month visit, I always commend her on sticking with it. To make her feel even better about her choice, I tell her about a study that compared adults who were breastfed as newborns versus those who were formula-fed. The study found a seven-point higher IQ in the group that was breast-fed.

Once, I was seeing a mom who I knew worked as an attorney and I decided to put an extra spin on the results. I said, "Seven IQ points, that is the difference between being a doctor and a lawyer."

She replied, "Hey! I am a lawyer!"

To which I said, "I didn't say which was smarter, just that there was a seven-point difference."

Even though breast milk is perfect for most babies, that doesn't mean there aren't some unique challenges associated with it. For example, many breastfeeding moms must watch what they eat in the first few months. Most foods that make us gassy will also give breastfed babies gas. So, while dads are eating whatever we want, moms are carefully choosing foods that won't make the baby grouchy.

Breast milk is also a bit thinner than formula, causing some babies to spit up. When a formula baby has reflux, we thicken their formula with cereal in the hopes that it will be held down better. That can't be done with breast milk, although once I pretended it could.

I had a mom who was particularly worried about her baby's reflux and I suggested, "You could thicken your milk by eating cereal."

Before I could tell her I was joking, she looked up excitedly and said, "I can? I am going to go get some Cheerios! No, I bet Raisin Bran would be better!"

She wasn't very happy with me when I told her eating cereal would not actually thicken her milk.

Another small downside to breast milk is that it causes higher levels of bilirubin, a condition called jaundice, to occur in newborns. This is usually easily treated with artificial light or, in many cases, by letting the baby sit in the sunlight coming in through a window. All pediatricians have seen a sunburned newborn so we are careful to emphasize the sunlight *through a window* part.

I was seeing a newborn baby with jaundice from breastfeeding and I told the mom we needed to do some sunlight therapy.

She said, "It makes me sad to think of him lying there naked all by himself. I am afraid he will be cold."

I told her she could sit with him and her reply was, "I have to sit naked by my picture window?"

Thankfully, her husband said what I was thinking, "Why would *you* need to be naked?"

We watched this information slowly sink in and then she yelled at him, "Give me some slack! I haven't had much sleep!"

Dad and I both looked at our feet and I quickly changed the subject.

5% CLUB!

TEENAGERS

It's NOT ONLY MY YOUNGER PATIENTS who make me laugh. Teens are also great comedians. Much of what they say is for shock value, which is great because I enjoy their attempts at shocking me. Nothing is off-limits as we go back-and-forth until the mom usually puts an end to it with a raised eyebrow reminding me that I am supposed to be an adult.

With my younger patients, the humorous situations often start with a child or parent misunderstanding things. With teens, the situations often begin with serious adult subjects but somewhere along the way we descend into fits of laughter.

During a well visit, I started to give two older teenage sisters my spiel on safe sex. I knew these girls for many years and mom was present for my discussion. I told them that birth control pills were not always effective and that approximately five percent of the time they fail.

Their mom then said, "You better listen to him. Both of you girls are here because of condom failures."

I was very embarrassed and looked at the girls to see if they were upset. On the contrary; they gave each other high fives and shouted, "Five percent club!"

That was not the reaction I was expecting but I was glad I was not going to have to refer them for counseling.

Around 2012, it became standard practice in my health organization to test all teens aged fifteen years and older for sexually transmitted infections (STIs) at each well visit. This is a simple test that only requires a urine sample but it created a lot of controversy in my clinic.

Some parents took issue with this test because state law requires us to only tell the patient the results of an STI test or a pregnancy test. As a parent, I understood this but we had to follow the law.

What we quickly learned is that teens rarely answer their phones. Our policy was after multiple failed attempts to reach the teen, we would send a certified letter asking them to call us. Most of the time, the result was negative, but we had to keep that confidential. Of course, getting the letter led to parents calling us, demanding to know if their teen had an STI.

Once, on Christmas morning, I received a call from a number I didn't recognize. When I answered, a quiet, teen male voice said, "Do I have gonorrhea?"

This was not how most telemarketers start their calls so I asked who was calling. It was a patient I had seen the month before who received the letter to call us about his STI test two weeks prior. He had wrongly assumed that because he received a letter, his urine was positive but he was too scared to call.

That morning, the pressure was too much and so he called me directly. He had my number saved from an x-ray report I had called him about two years earlier (another reason doctors hate to use our cell phones for work calls). I was happy to tell him to have a Merry Christmas and that he was STI-free.

On a different occasion, a teen actually answered his phone and when my nurse told him his urine was negative, he replied, "So, there were no drugs in it?"

I made a mental note to discuss drugs with him at his next visit.

One big reason teen well visits are very different from their younger counterparts is that I give them "the talk." This can be about sex, risky behaviors, alcohol, drugs, or all the above. I have given the talk thousands of times but it usually varies based on the teen's age and maturity level.

Needless to say, I hear more than I bargain for at times. Some teens treat me like a priest telling me all about their transgressions. These are the visits when I sometimes have to look at my watch and say, "I think that's enough for today. Let's pick up where we left off next time."

I have other teens that remind me of professional spies with their ability to withhold information. I have had teenage girls tell me they have never even kissed a guy much less had sexual intercourse, while I am showing them a positive pregnancy test!

One of my funniest experiences giving the talk was with a fifteen-year-old male named Jim. Jim was very shy and I would be willing to bet that he had never even held a girl's hand. I knew things would change one day, however, so I told him about condoms and birth control. I liked to drive home my point by telling my patients that the county we live in has one of the highest rates of teen pregnancies.

For reasons that I still do not know today, I added, "That means that the females in this county are more likely to be sexually active so I need you to be careful."

Jim's eyes got very big and he said, "Where are these girls!?" as if there was some secret club or hangout for which I could give him the directions!

Jim did not leave this visit any wiser about the dangers of teen sex but he did seem to have more hope for the future!

When I was young (yes, I hear what that sounds like … get me my cane), marijuana was mainly used by "stoners." Stoners rarely showered, dressed in dark clothes, and stayed off to themselves.

Teens today face a different reality. Drug use is common in every clique but especially with athletes. I even had a patient tell me that pot was common in the Future Farmers of America Club. You can insert your own joke about growing it here.

One of my patients was on the football team at a local high school and I asked him about marijuana use among the other players. He assured me that he had not heard of anyone on the team using that drug. I found this hard to believe and asked him again, telling him lots of players on the team had admitted to me it was common.

He said, "I promise! There is no marijuana. But there are a lot of people who smoke weed!"

Often when I talk to teens about marijuana use, I like to share with them the statistic that one in three teens will use weed during high school. On one occasion, I was seeing a fourteen-year-old male named Noah and I decided to change the way I worded this fact.

"Noah, picture your two best friends. Statistically, one of you is going to smoke weed during high school."

He thought about this for a few seconds. Then his eyes became very wide and he exclaimed, "I think it is going to be me!"

His mom practically screamed, "What?"

He looked very serious and said, "My two best friends are really good people. I can't see them doing drugs, so it must be me."

With a big sigh of relief, I explained to them that this was just a statistic and it did not mean that one of them *had* to do drugs.

Once, I had a teen "confess" to me about his drug use when I wasn't even asking him anything about it.

He was seventeen and in the office for a well visit. I noticed right away that he seemed very anxious so I started with an easy question, "How is school going?"

He looked up and quickly answered, "I don't smoke weed."

I laughed and patted him on the shoulder and told him we had not gotten to that part yet.

Five-year-olds and teens. I never know what they are going to say.

One of the most anxiety-provoking parts of a well visit for a patient is when I discuss what vaccine they are due for. It always amazes me that some of my most needle-phobic patients are teenage boys. So, naturally I enjoy torturing them about vaccines that do not exist or that they do not need.

One of our vaccines for Human Papillomavirus (HPV) can be given to both sexes. But, during the time I was seeing a teenage male, the vaccine was marketed for females as a cervical cancer preventative. I told the teen he needed this shot and he was livid.

He argued that he had never heard of it. He crossed his arms and said we couldn't make him take it. His mom, who knew about this vaccine, joined in the ruse and encouraged him to think of his health.

I added, "If you don't get this shot, your cervix could get cancer!"

He threw his arms in the air and said, "Fine! Just give it to me."

He was not very happy with us when we explained he didn't have a cervix! Little did I know, in a few short years it would become standard of care to give this vaccine to boys as well. HPV is now known to be a cause of oral and throat cancer, so we vaccinate boys, too.

Many times, when I explain this to parents they ask the question, "How does HPV get in the throat?"

I have yet to have to answer as the lightbulb always turns on followed by an "Oh!" and the subject is quickly changed.

I take pride in my ability to make my patients laugh and enjoy themselves. The toughest group to get a smile out of is often teenage girls. When I walk in and see a surly female, I take it as a personal challenge.

I was seeing a seventeen-year-old Black female for a well visit and she did not want to be there. She hardly spoke to me and despite all my jokes, I could not break through that stone facade. So, I finally gave up. I was filling out her sports form and I asked what sport she was going to play.

She replied she needed the form for a hip-hop dance class.

I said, "Oh, hip-hop, do you dance to 'Royals'?" which was my favorite song at the time by Lorde.

The mom asked if "Royals" was hip-hop and at the same time I said yes, the teen emphatically said no.

I looked at her and said, "It is hip-hop to me and I am really White!"

Like an iceberg cracking, the teen's face smiled and she broke into hysterical laughter. I was glad I had gotten through to her but I wasn't joking. I thought "Royals" was a hip-hop song.

I do admit that teens are a fun group to tease. With younger kids, I risk making them cry but teens can usually hold their own. A particular favorite torture method is telling them they are going to get the vaccine in their bottom (bum, buttocks, insert your favorite word here ... I have never liked the word bottom).

Sometimes, I take a different approach by asking if they want nurse Margaret to give their vaccine, explaining that she is very gentle and prefers the upper arm. Or, perhaps they would like our new male nurse, Mr. Dover, to give it to them. I then explain his first name is Ben and he prefers a different area to give shots!

Some teens get it instantly, some have to have it spelled out to them. Either way, they always beg for Margaret. I did have one young sibling hear that joke and say, "Hey, Ben Dover. He goes to my school." (I am very sorry, Ben).

A quick word about Margaret. She gave vaccines in my office for more than twenty-five years! Talk about a thankless job. Some of my patients called her "Mean Margaret" because they only knew her as the person who gave them shots. However, she is one of the nicest people I have ever met.

She told me once she was walking in the mall and a small boy she didn't recognize ran up and kicked her in the shin! He disappeared before she could even ask why he did it, but I think we all know.

WINNIE-THE-POO

Being a pediatrician means you must be comfortable talking about poo. And I don't mean Winnie!

Constipation is a frequent occurrence in children and I ask about it at almost every wellness check. If the kid is old enough to understand I will ask them, "Do you have any problems with Winnie-the-Poo?"

Most of the children look confused and say, "What?" then the parent will smile and answer the question for them.

One of my first experiences with the "joys" of constipation came during my training. I was a wet-behind-the-ears first-year resident when I was asked to get a history from a nine-year-old male named Andre who was being admitted with severe constipation.

In those days, it was common to admit children with constipation to the hospital for a "clean out." A clean out is a procedure to treat constipation when a child has failed outpatient medicines. These were very unpleasant admissions for all involved as the child had to ingest huge amounts of a liquid laxative called Golytely. *I always thought this should be called Goheavily, but no one asked my opinion.*

By the time I got up to Andre's room, he had consumed two bottles of Golytely. I knew my time with him might be cut short by a rather important call from Mother Nature, so I got right to taking his history.

I was halfway through when he got the first of his many calls and announced he had to go to the bathroom. I chatted with his mom awkwardly as we pretended neither of us could hear the grunting coming from the bathroom.

Andre then called out, "Mom, I think I stopped up the toilet."

We both went into the bathroom. I will spare you the description (I still have nightmares about it), but suffice it to say it was definitely stopped up. I told him not to worry about it and one of the nurses came in and called maintenance.

In many hospitals, maintenance would come two days later, but this was a private hospital and luckily, five minutes later, two maintenance guys showed up and headed straight to the bathroom with the confident gait usually only seen in fighter pilots.

I'm trying to take a history from this family, and they were in the bathroom scratching their heads and loudly discussing this baffling problem.

Finally, they called another worker on their walkie-talkie, who soon arrived with a plunger. After five minutes, one worker left and came back with a bigger plunger.

Another call on the walkie-talkie brought two more workers with a long snakelike tool. Each time a new person passed, Andre's face became redder and redder.

Finally, I heard cheers and high fives as if they had just won the Super Bowl. The "team" left while patting each other on the back, with the last one giving Andre a thumbs-up. By this point he had the covers pulled up to his eyes and was trying not to be seen.

I have never forgotten that dear child, but I hope he has blocked the entire episode from his memory.

Oddly enough, I had another interesting episode of a constipated child in the same hospital later that year (I wonder if children eat more cheese in this town).

I was assigned to a general pediatric clinic when a child walked in smelling like he had rolled in cow manure. He was seven-years-old and went by the name of Nathaniel.

When I walked into the room, I had an impulse not to close the door as I didn't want to be enclosed with this smell. But it is poor form to discuss someone's medical history with the door open so I reluctantly closed it.

The smell was almost unbearable. The entire room smelled like stool. The smell seemed to be emanating from his skin and breath.

I quickly learned that Nathaniel had come to the clinic today because of chronic abdominal pain.

I asked the mom the obvious question, "Is he having any trouble stooling?"

"Oh, he rarely stools." She replied.

I then asked the mom how often he had a BM (actually that doesn't sound like me—I probably asked how often he pooped).

They brought their heads close together and whispered for a moment. The mom then looked up and said, "The last time he pooped was eleven months ago."

I gave a nervous chuckle and said, "Seriously?"

She nodded and said, "Yes. We remember because it was right after his birthday."

I was shocked but fearing that I only had a few more minutes before the last of the fresh oxygen would be gone, I asked him to lay on the bed so I could examine him.

I was not prepared for what I felt. His entire abdomen was swollen but incredibly firm from his ribs down to his hips. It felt like a wooden shield had been implanted under the skin.

I knew I was in over my head and went to get my attending physician. As I told him the story, he smiled all-knowingly like attendings are prone to do and pronounced, "I am sure it is not that bad. She must be mistaken about how long it has been since he stooled."

I felt a little better and laughed half-heartedly, "Yes. That must be it."

I wish I had a camera when my attending felt Nathaniel's belly. His eyes grew large and he began pushing harder trying to penetrate the "poop shield." He then stuttered for a second before looking at Nathaniel and asking, "You haven't had a stool in eleven months?"

"Nope," was the only reply.

It turns out that the child was homeschooled and rarely left the house. His mom had gotten used to the horrible smell and felt his lack of stooling was something better to be ignored than addressed.

Nathaniel was admitted to the hospital and taken to surgery. And yes, because I was the first one to see him (and because I was an intern and lowest on the totem pole), I was nominated to assist in the surgery.

I will not tell you how the stool was removed, but will reveal that twenty-four pounds of it were carted out of the operating room that day. I will never forget that it was one nurse's job to continuously spray Lysol into the air during the entire procedure.

If only Nathaniel's mom had read him the book *Everyone Poops* by Taro Gomi, when he was little, maybe he could have been spared this experience. As for me, I can't smell Lysol without thinking back to that traumatic day.

I was reminded of the story a few years later when I was taking care of another child with constipation.

Seth was a six-year-old child who I was seeing in my clinic for constipation. His mom was telling me that he cried when he had a BM because his stools were so large.

I asked Seth's mother when was the last time he had had a stool and he interjected, "Never again, if I can help it!"

I considered telling him about Nathaniel but knew that would only give him nightmares. I then thought I should write a cautionary tale in the vein of "The Kid Who Cried Wolf." I wanted to call it "The Kid Who Never Pooped" but couldn't see it catching on.

One of the most frequent calls I get at the office is about constipation in one- to two-month-old babies. Newborns poop reflexively, usually every time they eat. However, at this age, they start gaining some control over this process.

Some babies are good at this, some not so much. The latter will strain and get very red in the face because they are effectively squeezing the exit door closed. The parents appropriately interpret this as constipation and call us.

The nurses are used to this and tell them it is normal and if the stools aren't hard, to just bicycle the infant's legs and help them relax.

On one memorable occasion, my nurse told a parent of a straining one-month old baby she could use a little pediatric suppository to help the baby stool. This is not wrong but just unnecessary as I described above.

These particular parents took things very literally and didn't quite understand the instructions.

I found this out when they came to see me three days later and the infant was having diarrhea. I asked the patient's father what was going on and he replied, "He used to be constipated, but now he has diarrhea."

He went on to say, "We followed your nurse's advice and used the suppositories even though she didn't tell us it would take so many for them to work."

I could see where this was going and even though I wasn't sure I wanted to know, I asked, "You used more than one?"

"Yeah, it took eight."

I looked to his wife to see if this was true and she said, "We put one in and nothing happened. So, we put another one in, he still didn't poop. He finally went after the eighth one. It was lucky he did as that was our last one! Now he has been having diarrhea since."

Dad's eyes suddenly widened and he asked, "Do you think them suppositories caused the diarrhea?"

I mentally crossed out four or five sarcastic replies before finally settling on, "Yes, I think that is likely the cause."

For those of you worrying about this baby, pediatric suppositories just act as a lubricant and do not contain any medicine. So, besides diarrhea, this baby was fine. However, given his parents' initial decision-making, his future may be a tad bit concerning.

Many times, when stool is involved, parents love to show you a picture. They feel like they can't describe it in enough detail (or maybe they figure I would love to look at a picture of their kid's poop).

I actually don't mind because it gives me a chance for one of my favorite one-liners: "Oh, you took a Snapcrap!"

Grandmothers don't find that one funny, by the way.

I remember the first time I used this joke; I was seeing a very adorable four-year-old named Jenna with constipation. Unfortunately, I picked the wrong audience for the unveiling of my new term, as this mom had a very serious personality and didn't even crack a pretend smile.

Feeling mildly defeated, I looked at the picture and told mom, "Yep, that IS a very large stool."

I was explaining how we were going to handle this problem when the little girl pulled on my sleeve and very quietly asked, "Do you want to hear about my stool?"

I replied, "I already heard about it, sweetie. I even saw a picture."

Undaunted, she went on to say, "It's shaped like a donut!"

I was a bit grossed out by that image and a bit confused as the stool I had seen looked like a brown tennis ball. I thought maybe this was like the situation where people see different things in clouds.

Without meaning to, I verbalized, "Ewww!"

The mom then looked up and with no sense of humor explained, "She is talking about the stool that she stands on at night to brush her teeth."

Unable to contain myself, I burst out laughing. Which, in turn, made the little girl laugh hysterically even though she didn't know what was so funny.

The mom just had a look on her face that said, "I wish I had chosen a more mature pediatrician."

I patted the girl on the head and told her sometime I would love to see *that* stool.

When I told my wife, Ellen, this story later that night her only question was, "Why would you think a four-year-old would use the word stool for poop?"

I had no idea but these are the visits that make me love my job!

My wife was proven correct about children's knowledge of the word stool just a few months later when I was seeing a five-year-old male named Jonathon for his annual checkup.

I had seen him a few months earlier for (you guessed it) constipation and given him a stool softener. I asked if things had improved.

His mom replied, "Oh yes! After about a week he was doing so much better."

She went on to say, "One day, I went into the bathroom to check on him. He was sitting on the toilet and lifted his legs up and said, 'See Mommy? I didn't use my stool! Dr. Benfield wouldn't let me.'"

It turns out the boy had been using a little wooden stool under his feet so he could get enough leverage to help get the poop out. When his mom asked, "What do you mean Dr. Benfield wouldn't let you?"

The little boy replied, "Dr. Benfield said I needed to stop having hard stools."

After twenty-three years in pediatrics, I have heard stool described every possible way. I will not gross you out with these descriptions but there was one that stood out.

I was seeing a patient who was constipated and I gave the mom my usual advice as well as a stool softener. I asked her to call and let my nurse know how her son was doing in a few days.

The mom called back and reported, "Things are going better. He had two great bowel movements right in a row. It looked like two sticks of butter."

I don't know whether it was yellow or rectangular, but two sticks of butter stool are not a mental image I wanted in my brain. I now pass that along to you.

As you can see, constipation is a frequently seen condition in my clinic. It is usually a pretty straightforward diagnosis. However, there are times when it can be tricky.

Early in my career when I was still a bit naive, I saw a five-year-old male with autism named Jackson. He was nonverbal, and this was my first time seeing him.

He was refusing to eat and holding his stomach. To make matters worse, his dad thought he felt a mass in his abdomen.

I had Jackson lay down and, sure enough, I did feel a large firm mass just above his belly button. Both the parents and I were very concerned.

I called in a favor with radiology and managed to get a same-day MRI of Jackson's abdomen. Usually, it would take over a week to get an MRI but I explained to the radiologist that I was afraid this patient had cancer so they worked him in.

When the MRI results came back, the mass was not cancer but, in fact, a large stool.

I was very embarrassed but also very relieved that the patient did not have cancer. It also taught me a lesson to get a more detailed history before jumping to such an expensive test.

I also did not make eye contact with that radiologist whenever I saw him in the hospital.

A couple of years later, I was seeing a seventeen-year-old female for a well visit when I felt a mass in her abdomen. I remembered my previous mistake and began asking her about her stooling history.

She assured me that she was not constipated. Going on to say that she usually stooled two to three times per day and it was always soft.

Now I was concerned and so again called for a "stat" MRI. As I sent the patient over to the hospital for the scan, my thoughts returned to Jackson.

Even though this patient did not sound constipated, I called and asked the radiologist to do a plain X-ray of her abdomen before the MRI.

Thirty minutes later, I received a call from the radiologist saying the X-ray showed that this patient had "the worst constipation I have ever seen."

We canceled the MRI and after three months of intense stool softeners, the patient's "mass" was gone.

I was quickly becoming an expert at diagnosing "poop tumors!" What did I learn from this experience? Always look for constipation first … and never trust a teenager!

THE PENIS

FIRST, I KNOW YOU ARE QUESTIONING how a literary gem such as this could have a chapter called "The Penis." But the truth is, questions about this body part come up more than any other part. And that is pretty impressive, given that only fifty percent of my patients have one!

Questions about the penis usually start at the first newborn visit. I often get asked if the circumcision looks right. The most common mom complaint is that the doctor who performed the circumcision didn't remove enough of the foreskin. This sometimes leads to some awkward conversations regarding the purpose of the foreskin which I will not include here.

During the next few visits, questions sometimes arise about the color of the head of the penis. At this age, the head of the penis can have a bit of a purplish hue. This is completely normal, but I have had a couple of moms take their babies to the emergency room at bath times because they are afraid the color is a sign of lack of oxygen.

Even when I am not answering questions about this body part during those first visits, it still seems to come up in funny ways. On one memorable day, I was doing a well visit on a two-week-old baby boy and I noticed his beautiful large blue eyes.

This reminded me of one of the more interesting things I learned during medical school. The colored part of the eye (the iris) never grows. That is why babies look like they have such huge eyes.

Often during well visits, I ask moms (and especially grandmothers, who like to think there is nothing they don't know about babies), "What is the only body part that never grows? In other words, what is the same size in a baby as in an adult?"

As I looked at this newborn's prominent eyes, I asked the mom the above question.

She thought about it for a second and then whispered, "the penis" (because you're not allowed to say that word out loud).

It is hard to embarrass a doctor, but I was so embarrassed I didn't even tell her the correct answer. I just looked away and said, "No, that's not it."

I just hope she didn't go home and tell her husband what she had said.

Moms are not the only ones who have issues with this body part. I noticed very early in my career that dads don't come to as many well visits after the first one or two. However, when the baby is a boy, they are often present at the four-month visit.

Why the sudden interest? Concern over the size (or lack thereof) of their son's penis. Babies get sort of chunky at this particular age because they are not mobile yet and all they do is eat and sleep. One of the chunkiest areas is the fat pad right above the penis. This makes the penis look smaller as the fat pad covers much of it. Sometimes, the baby is so heavy that the penis disappears in the fat pad completely!

Needless to say, this makes dads very anxious. Some fathers make it all the way to the halfway point of the visit before asking if their child's penis has shrunk. More commonly, as soon as I walk in, I hear, "Doc, I have a question."

I usually answer, "Don't worry. Your son's penis is fine," before they can even ask.

I would be remiss if I didn't admit that the size of the child's penis is also a common question as the child gets older.

One day, I was examining a very obese five-year-old. When I looked at his genitals, his mom said, "Yeah, he's got a real short penis. They say it is because he is so heavy that it kind of hides it, but I still think it is small."

Before I could defend his "honor," the boy looked at me, grinned, and said, "When I mess with it, it gets longer."

This was followed by a brief awkward silence. Then, before the child could give us any more details, I quickly changed the subject.

The illusion of the shrinking penis can also affect males when they are older if they don't watch their weight. The following story is so unbelievable that if it didn't happen to me, I wouldn't believe it was true.

It was a normal Friday afternoon when I received a call from an orthopedic surgeon in Charlotte. I only knew the physician by name and had never spoken to him. My nurse said he was seeing one of my patients that I did not know well named Jamie and that he needed to speak to me urgently.

The doctor was seeing Jamie for scoliosis. The call went like this, "I'm seeing a patient of yours and he's morbidly obese. He weighs about 240 pounds and he's only thirteen-years-old."

I thought he was going to lecture me on getting this patient to lose weight but he continued with, "But that's not why I am calling you. Given that he has scoliosis I thought I should check his Tanner stage."

A Tanner stage is basically checking the patient's privates. It stages how far into puberty the patient is based on how much pubic hair they have and the size of their testicles. It is relevant when you're checking for scoliosis to know their Tanner stage, as scoliosis can increase dramatically at the beginning and at the end of puberty.

My interest was starting to fade when he hit me with the reason for the call. "I finally got him to agree to have me check him down there and when I looked . . . well, I really don't know how to put this, but he has female genitalia."

I almost dropped the phone. All I could think to say was, "What?" as I tried to decide if this was a prank call. The problem was that the doctor on the other line had a Boston accent and I didn't know anyone from there.

I then asked, "What did his mom say about that?"

"Oh, she was quite surprised!"

Then I remembered that he said the patient was obese and I began to understand what was happening. I told him, "I think he has a hidden penis because of his weight. The area you think is a vagina is actually his scrotum. Push down on the area above the 'female genitalia' and the penis should pop right out."

He began to stutter and finally got out, "I am an orthopedist and not that comfortable with that area."

My thoughts were, *first of all, you are a doctor, and secondly, you are a man and have those parts!*

He told me he would rather have me do that part of the examination. Since it was Friday afternoon, he suggested that I see them in my office on Monday. I was not about to let this child and his mother go through the weekend wondering where his penis went. I said to the surgeon, "Tell them to come straight to my office. I will wait for them."

They made the sixty-minute drive from Charlotte in forty-five minutes. I met them in the waiting room to find both of them with tears in their eyes. I led them into an exam room, had Jamie drop his drawers, and pushed on his fat pad.

Out popped his penis like a groundhog on Groundhog Day. I looked at mom and said, "Congratulations, you have a boy!"

They were both overjoyed and the mom could not speak. Jamie just avoided any eye contact as he said, "Thanks."

So many questions. Why didn't Jamie just tell the orthopedic surgeon, "I have a penis!" Where did his mom think his penis had gone? As I said, this was an unbelievable story.

I never sent another patient to that orthopedist and I hope Jamie has blocked this incident from his memory.

When I first joined the children's clinic, I performed circumcisions on the newborns at the hospital. Many moms would ask if they could watch the circumcision. I find it interesting that I never had one dad ask that question.

I would always say no to this request. I was not worried about the moms becoming upset at seeing their babies in pain, because we use lidocaine to numb the penis and most babies sleep through the procedure.

The truth is the thought of having a mom watch me makes me incredibly nervous. Not to mention the fact that I am not sure most moms could stomach watching an area of their baby being removed.

However, on one Saturday morning, I told a mom she could watch because I knew her well and she told me she was a nurse and had worked in an operating room.

Right before I started, I looked over at her and asked if she was sure she could handle this.

She replied, "Of course, I see way worse things than this in the O.R. all the time.

So, I leaned over the baby and said, "I am going to make an incision with my scalpel right here."

The next sound was her hitting the floor. The newborn nursery nurse helped her to a chair and as she was going to get the mom some water, I heard the nurse murmur, "I told him he shouldn't let anyone watch."

And that was the last time I allowed a mom to sit in on that procedure.

During every well visit, it is standard to check a boy's privates to make sure he is developing appropriately and not having any issues. This tends to cause a lot of embarrassment. I try to relieve this by saying funny things as I check them.

My most common technique is to ask, "Do you know why I need to check your privates?" as they are unbuttoning their pants. This makes them forget their bashfulness and they usually answer, "To make sure everything is alright."

I then tell them, "No. The real reason I check is because sometimes when boys are playing outside, a part can 'fall off.' Often, the part is never found and I am just making sure that didn't happen to you!"

While the kids are laughing (although I admit one or two have started crying instead) I get the exam done before they even realize what has happened. Most of my patients have heard my spiel and as soon as I ask, "Why do I check your privates?" They yell, "to make sure nothing fell off!"

On one memorable occasion, I was seeing a five-year-old boy for his well checkup and his six-year-old brother, Larson, was with him. Larson was talking a mile per minute and was obviously enjoying the fact that he was not being checked that day.

When I said my "falling off" line to his brother, Larson suddenly became silent and subtly moved his hand down over his privates.

He was not subtle enough as his mom said, "What are you checking there, buddy?"

Sometimes, instead of using the falling off line, as I am examining boys I will say, "Everything looks normal down here. I see you have one of these and three of those." Again, this lightens the mood and makes the child laugh.

However, this backfired a bit once when I was examining an eleven-year-old male and said this about him. He laughed but I turned around to see his five-year-old sister staring at me with very wide eyes.

I had forgotten she was there when I made my comment and I said, "Sweetheart, I am sorry about that."

She handled it well and in a loud voice replied, "Someone better tell Dad!"

My attempts to make this part of the exam less stressful do not always work as intended. One time, I was examining a four-year-old boy and I asked, "What do you call this part?"

He replied, "I don't know what it's called but I know what my daddy calls it!"

His mom and I both yelled, "NO!"

We were too late and he yelled, "NUTS!"

I looked at his mom and she was as relieved as I was—*that could have been much worse.*

There are, of course, more proper ways to describe this area when talking to patients but I have always liked the term "privates." It is a word everyone knows without being crude.

I have never liked the word "genitals" and, to my knowledge, have never said it out loud. I was writing a script once on the computer and saw a funny description of the word. I was writing for steroid cream and the computer gave me options for instructions that would print on the patient's prescription.

My favorite option was, "Do not apply to genitals (the area under your underwear)."

So, if you ever needed to define that word, here is your answer.

The group of patients that hates the "privates" exam the most is definitely boys between the ages of ten and fourteen. Some will outright refuse to let me check the area. It is the rare patient who gets through this without a red face.

One evening after work, I was helping the local middle school by giving free sports physicals. I was in a classroom and there was a long line of young football players outside waiting.

Every time one boy would leave the room, I would hear the next boy coming in whispering, "Did he check your privates?" or "Did he look down there?"

Overhearing, I would laugh and say, "Yes, I did, and I am going to check yours, too!"

I always felt these sports physicals at the school were incomplete as I didn't have a parent to ask questions about the child's history. This was difficult as most males this age did not know anything about their health history.

One of the males tried to pretend he knew more than he did during one of these exams. As I was getting ready to check his privates I asked. "Have you ever had a hernia?"

He quickly and emphatically answered no. I asked if he even knew what a hernia was and he replied, "No, but I know I have never had one!"

On the same day, I was seeing another football player and he was sweating. He was so nervous.

I was reading his form and I said, "Well, it says here you do not have lung or heart problems and no history of hospitalizations. So, you're healthy?"

He shrugged his shoulders and said, "I don't know." And then looked at me and said, "My mama says I am."

I have noticed that even though many of my patients don't pay close attention to me when I am explaining their illness to their parents, this is not the case if I am discussing a male's penis. This was evident when I was seeing a six-year-old male with irritation to that area from his swim suit.

I told his dad, "I want you to apply some Vaseline to the rash a couple of times per day."

The child looked very worried and said, "You are going to burn my wiener?"

Dad and I stared at each other for a few seconds until dad realized the issue. "Vaseline. Not gasoline!"

This isn't exactly about the penis, but a close neighbor. The story begins when I was performing a well check on a one-year-old male named Andre. It was my first time seeing Andre. After I finished examining him, I reported to mom that he looked great.

She responded that she was glad he looked good because he was scheduled to have abdominal surgery in two days.

I was not aware of this and so asked her what kind of surgery was involved.

She said, "For his undescended testicles. His testicles are still in his abdomen and they are going to do surgery to pull them back down."

She was explaining she couldn't sleep because of worrying about the surgery when she noticed me looking at her like she was crazy.

I said, "Undescended testicles? He's got testicles."

Now it was her turn to look at me like I was crazy and say, "No, he doesn't. He wasn't born with them!"

I opened the diaper and showed her Andre's two testicles that were down where they were supposed to be.

It turns out this was the first time they had been down. Mom said they weren't there when she gave him a bath the night before.

I didn't do anything to make them come down, it just happened that two days before he was going to have surgery, his testicles decided to drop. This is why doctors typically wait until the boy is one year old to do the surgery because sometimes it takes that long for them to appear.

This baby decided to wait 363 days after birth, but at least now he would not have to have surgery.

The baby's mom thanked me profusely and even though I explained to her that I had nothing to do with the dropping, she still gave me the credit.

I know this because he returned a few months later with his mom and grandmother and the grandmother asked, "Is this the doctor that got Andre's testicles to drop?" (Okay, she said "nuts" but this is a family book).

bonjour
hello
ciao
olá
hola

LANGUAGE BARRIERS

My practice is in a small southern town and, therefore, unlike some of my colleagues in big cities, I don't see a lot of international patients. However, I do have many Hispanic patients and I absolutely love taking care of this population.

I find that my Hispanic parents are quick to laugh and have an easygoing way about them that I enjoy. Another admirable trait is that Hispanic moms tend not to worry as much about the "what ifs" of parenting. For example, they rarely ask questions like, "Could this be cancer?" or "Can we check some labs?" They also usually follow my instructions to the letter.

When I first joined the Shelby Children's Clinic in 1999, there were no interpreters available via phone or video like we have now. Luckily, we had a nurse who spoke Spanish. Unfortunately, on days she wasn't there our visits with Spanish-speaking patients could be an adventure.

During one memorable visit, a Hispanic mom who did not speak any English came in with her newborn son. Not only did my nurse not speak Spanish, but she made the situation worse by her attempts to communicate with the mom. For some reason, she thought yelling at the poor lady in English but with a Spanish accent was the best way to get her point across.

I heard her clear across the clinic. "Now we're going to weigh-o the baby-o and so remove the diaper-o from the baby-o."

When the mom didn't understand, my nurse decided speaking louder was going to help.

Luckily, my nurse practitioner partner, Laurie Horsely, who speaks Spanish, heard all the yelling and came in to take over the visit. We all yelled when we spoke to my nurse for the rest of the week to make our point.

During my training at UNC, I was often encouraged to see Spanish-speaking patients in the hospital because I took Spanish in high school. However, I only took it during my first two years of high school and when I arrived at college, I placed right back into Spanish 1. Instead of starting over, I decided to take two semesters of Portuguese (that's a long story) and, as a result, my Spanish was really quite limited.

Unfortunately, I still spoke more Spanish than most of my colleagues and so I was dubbed "El Elegido" which means "The Chosen One."

One night when I was on call in the hospital, I was asked to see a three-year-old patient with pneumonia. Before I went in, one of the nurses said, "By the way, the mom doesn't speak any English."

I replied, "No worries. I will get the translator on the phone in the room."

After I had the interpreter set up, I explained what pneumonia was, how it was treated, and what the mom could expect while her child was in the hospital.

When the interpreter repeated my instructions, the mom sat staring straight ahead.

I decided to show off my Spanish and said, "*Preguntas*? (Questions?)"

Again, the mom sat staring straight at me without any indication she was hearing me. This was getting uncomfortable when a thought came to me. *I wonder if this mom is deaf? I need to find someone who knows sign language.*

As I got up to leave, the mom suddenly spoke a full thirty seconds of words that I had never heard. Now, it was me staring silently at her. At last, I heard the translator on the phone say, "I am not sure, but I think that was Laotian."

I looked at the mom who was emphatically shaking her head yes.

I repeated the visit but this time with a Laotian interpreter. When I went back to the nursing station and admitted what I had done, everyone had a good laugh at my expense.

In the nurse's defense, she did not say the patient's mom spoke Spanish, only that she didn't speak English.

Over the next three days, I got to know this family well and even picked up the Laotian words for hello and goodbye. And no, I do not remember how to say them now.

I have always felt I am a magnet for circumstances like the one above. Later that year, I was working in the resident training clinic and was again thrust into a confusing situation.

At this clinic, my job was to obtain a history and physical from a patient and then report my findings to my attending physician. The child I was seeing on this particular day was a five-year-old Asian girl named Lyn. She was accompanied by both of her parents, two siblings, and a Hispanic lady who looked to be in her thirties.

I was confused who the Hispanic lady was so I asked the little girl, "Who did you bring with you today?"

She replied, "This is my dad, this is my mom, and these are my brothers. I do not know who this lady is!"

As we all turned to look at her, the lady began speaking rapidly in Spanish and pointing to the door.

Thankfully at that moment, a nurse opened the door and said, "We are missing a patient from the adult clinic and are checking each room for her."

The little girl exclaimed, "She is here! She is here!"

Evidently, she was in the waiting room waiting for her sister who was being seen in another clinic. Somehow, she was told to come into this room by mistake. She had been sitting with Lyn's family for about five minutes before I came in. I can't imagine how confused they all were.

As I mentioned, my fluency in Spanish left a lot to be desired when I entered practice. However, it has improved dramatically, thanks to practicing my language skills over the years with my Hispanic families. I love attempting to speak Spanish to their children and watching them laugh as I get the words wrong.

In the last few years, I have noticed that Hispanic children don't know Spanish as well as in the past. I think this is a combination of the fact that their parents are often born in the United States and most of what they hear on television is in English.

When I meet a family like this, I always encourage the parents to make sure the children hold on to their culture and learn to speak the language fluently. I encourage Hispanic moms with new babies to speak both English and Spanish to their babies.

Therefore, when I see a Hispanic child, I speak Spanish with them not only for fun, but also to see if they are learning it themselves.

Recently, I was seeing a seven-year-old child with the last name Garcia. I asked him my usual list of questions in Spanish and he did not understand any of them.

After a few minutes of this I looked at his mother and said, "Why is he not learning Spanish?"

She replied in an angry voice, "Because we are from Brazil!"

She was not happy with my assumption that they were Spanish-speaking. The few words I remembered from my college Portuguese class did not impress her, either.

The rest of the visit was a bit tense and I made sure not to repeat my mistake in subsequent visits.

On another occasion, two children, ages five and three, came in for a well checkup. Their mom spoke English and Spanish well, but dad only spoke English. I asked mom how fluent the children were in Spanish.

She replied, "I am embarrassed to admit this but they mostly only know bad words."

I gave her my best attempt at a raised eyebrow and she explained, "Because my husband does not speak Spanish, I don't speak it much at home. However, when he gets on my nerves, I often say very ugly things in Spanish and the kids are picking up some of the words!"

I have always found it interesting that one of the first words an English-speaking baby says is "Da Da" while in a Spanish-speaking family, the baby will say "Pa Pa."

This is not because they hear this word often, because even in homes with no father a baby's first word is usually "Da Da." Rather, a father is called Da Da because that is one of a baby's first consonant sounds.

Why do they first say "Pa Pa" in Spanish-speaking families? Is it genetic or is the Spanish language that they hear during their first year predisposing them to this consonant sound? Not too long ago, I had an interesting way to study this question.

One of my English-speaking families adopted a Hispanic newborn. The family spoke a little bit of Spanish but used primarily English around the baby during the first year. The baby's first word? "Da Da."

So, based on my research on one family, it is the language the baby hears that causes the difference. To date, *The New England Journal of Medicine* has not reached out to me to publish this "study."

Another way for me to practice my Spanish is with my own children who took the language in high school. It has been especially fulfilling to watch my oldest daughter, Keeley, go from a high school student just starting in Spanish to finishing college with a minor in Spanish. I initially helped her with pronouncing words, but was quickly passed in fluency and now call her when I need help.

Her new knowledge also led to an embarrassing gaffe on my part. When she was very young, I heard someone say to a little girl, "*Gracias, muchisimo.*"

I liked that and would occasionally call Keeley my little "muchisimo."

During her first-year learning Spanish, she came home and asked me, "Dad, why do you call me muchisimo?"

I explained that it meant little girl, but she emphatically let me know that I was wrong and that I had actually been calling her "very much" all this time!

It did not help my case when I added that she was "very much" trouble when she was little.

My clinic has been fortunate to employ Hispanic nurses over the years. This has been especially helpful to our Spanish-speaking patients as well as to me. They taught me many medical Spanish phrases as well as a few insults to use on my children.

I am sure this was not always as enjoyable for the nurses as was the case when I tried to wish one of them Happy New Year by exclaiming, "Feliz Ano Nuevo!"

I knew I had messed up when her eyes got huge and her face turned red. She quietly corrected me, "Año, not Ano!"

I wasn't sure I wanted to know but I asked her what I had said.

"Happy New Anus."

I profusely apologized and have not wished this to anyone again!

My last miscommunication story is a doozy. I was seeing a newborn with a mom and dad who only spoke Spanish and so I had an interpreter on the phone helping me. At the end of the visit, I asked if they had any questions. The dad replied that they needed to see Phyllis.

We didn't have anyone in my office with that name so I asked the interpreter to ask the dad who Phyllis was.

After a lengthy discussion between the two of them, the interpreter reported that when they were in the hospital after giving birth the nurse said, "If you have any concerns about chlamydia, gonorrhea, or syphilis, you will need to be seen in the clinic."

What the dad heard was, "If you have concerns about chlamydia or gonorrhea, see Phyllis!"

Well, the dad had concerns, but I didn't know where I was going to find Phyllis!

MY FOOT IN MY MOUTH

As I SAT DOWN TO WRITE this chapter, I was honestly a bit embarrassed by the number of stories that instead of being funny things children or their parents said, were stories of me saying or doing the wrong thing. We all remember stories where we have screwed up, but seeing the sheer volume of mine on paper was quite shocking.

My wife tried to make me feel better by reminding me that because I spend eight-to-ten hours per day talking to people, I am bound to say the wrong thing now and then. I think the truth is that I have a small mischievous part of my brain that loves to get me in trouble. It is very adept at tricking my mouth into saying things when the rest of my brain is paying attention to medical details.

This chapter is being written by that part of my brain so I am not responsible for the following stories.

One of my most memorable "foot in mouth" moments involved a teen with depression. Even though it was fifteen years ago, I still cringe when I think about this visit. The teen was named Sharon and she was accompanied by her mom.

We had been talking for a bit about how stressed she felt when I asked, "Sharon, what is the biggest stress in your life?"

She pointed to her mom and said, "She is always on my case about making good grades and doing my homework."

This hit a nerve with me because I agree with this style of parenting. I told her that if my parents hadn't stayed on me, instead of wearing this white coat I would be asking, "Do you want fries with that?"

I was quite pleased with my analogy but as soon as I said it, both of their faces changed and they kind of startled. I knew immediately I had said the wrong thing.

I looked at mother and daughter, trying to figure out my mistake and I noticed what was written across the mom's shirt . . . Hardee's! For those of you not from the South, this is a local fast-food restaurant where the mom obviously worked.

I had not noticed this when they arrived but my mischievous brain nemesis certainly noticed.

I should have apologized, but I was too embarrassed. My only consolation is that I am sure her mom would agree with my sentiment that neither of us want her daughter making a career serving in the fast-food industry. I know, it's a stretch.

As bad as that moment was, it was not the worst slip of my tongue. This blunder occurred on a day when I was seeing a teenage mom for an initial weight check with her newborn boy.

The baby had been circumcised in the hospital and during this initial visit I always teach the parent how to care for the penis to prevent adhesions. Adhesions occur in newborn males when the foreskin reattaches itself to the head of the penis. This can be prevented by routinely pulling the foreskin back from the head of the penis during the first few months of life.

It is important to preface this story by saying that when I perform a circumcision in the hospital, I always explain the procedure to the parents beforehand. The baby is usually still in the nursery, so I show the parents what I am going to do by using my index finger as a prop. I finish my explanation by showing them with my finger prop how to pull back the foreskin as above.

So, on this fateful day I opened the baby's diaper and said, "Let me show you how to take care of the baby's circumcision." As I opened the baby's diaper, I noticed he had an erection (which, as you parents know, is a sure sign the baby has to pee).

I said, "Oh, my gosh, he is about to pee. Let me just show you ON ME."

The mom's eyes got huge and she let out a very nervous laugh. I then pictured the speech bubble of what I had just said and let out my own nervous laugh.

Even after explaining that I meant by using my finger, the damage was done. The mom could not look me in the eye. Can you really blame her?

I have a low tolerance for boredom and one of my tricks to keep this at bay is to read fake medical complaints off the chart as I walk into a room. It usually makes the children laugh and keeps me entertained. However, it also caused a horrible mix-up once with a teenage patient.

I was seeing a sixteen-year-old girl for the first time for a possible urinary tract infection. To lighten the mood, I looked at her chart and said, "So, you need me to give you the talk about boys."

I looked up and waited for the inevitable smile and shaking of the head. Instead, the young patient almost fell off the table.

Her eyes widened and she demanded, "What? Are you serious? For real?"

I wasn't sure why this made her so upset so I quickly told her I was kidding and that I needed to hear about her urinary symptoms.

She held her hand on her chest and said, "I am going to need a moment."

Her mom and I looked at each other confused. Finally, the patient told me about her symptoms. After looking in the computer and seeing her labs, I told the patient that she indeed had a UTI and I would send in an order for antibiotics.

I then apologized that my earlier comment upset her and she admitted, "I thought you were saying I was pregnant!"

My mind finally caught up to her. She had, after all, given me a urine specimen and thought I had used it for a pregnancy test. Not only that, my big mouth made her think it was positive!

I gave a quick nervous laugh and apologized for the mix-up. Then, her mom suddenly said, "Wait. Are you sexually active?"

I found something interesting to look at in the computer as the teen stuttered her way through a denial saying, "I thought it was some sort of *Jane the Virgin* situation."

Somehow, this terrible excuse landed and the mom seemed to buy it replying, "Oh, good."

I was mortified at this chain of events but felt better when my nurse heard them laughing as they went up the hall with the mom adding, "I like him."

Well, I didn't like me very much at that point. And yes, that was the last time I used that line on a teenager.

If you are hoping that most of my gaffes occurred when I was a young, naive pediatrician, I can unfortunately admit that is not the case. This next visit occurred only recently and involves a patient with high functioning autism named Curtis.

Curtis was at the clinic for his eighteen-year-old well visit and arrived for his appointment without his parents. This was no big deal, as I had been caring for him since he was an infant and knew him well.

First, let me tell you a little about Curtis. Because of his diagnosis, he doesn't understand humor or sarcasm well and at times can be a little robotic. I found his personality unique and refreshing and enjoyed talking to him.

During teen well visits, I like to discuss drugs. So, I asked, "Do any of your friends vape?"

Curtis replied with no emotion, "I don't have any friends."

I felt horrible for him and quickly tried to think of something to help him. Suddenly it came to me and I said, "You could go to church. I bet you would meet lots of people in a youth group."

He stared straight ahead and said, "I am an atheist."

Now, I was frazzled. I hear about plenty of sensitive topics from my teen patients—gender identity, homosexuality, drug use, suicidal thoughts—and I can handle these without much problem. But this statement shocked me and I didn't know how to reply.

The next thing I knew, my nemesis brain made my mouth say, "Well, does that group not get together?"

There was a very awkward silence while he considered this before replying, "I am not really sure."

I wish this was the end of the story, but as I was finishing up, Curtis commented that he wished he was taller.

I told him, "Don't worry about it, that is just how God made you."

He kind of twitched and turned to look at me. I froze and told my brain, *don't cover it, don't cover it.* Instead, I heard myself say, "Or however else you think you got here."

Even as I type this, I am cringing but, hey, this is how God made *me*. Luckily, my comment didn't seem to bother him. We ended this horrible visit with him asking if he could continue coming to see me, even though he was now an adult.

As I look back on my embarrassing moments, I realize many of them occur when I am trying to be funny or clever. Even though I know this gets me into trouble, I simply cannot help myself.

One time, I was giving a mom of a teenage girl parenting tips. I explained to her that rules are very important, but she didn't want to be so strict that her daughter would rebel.

That is perfect pediatric advice, but I couldn't leave well enough alone. I had to add, "We all know how preacher's daughters can be."

Instead of laughing, she looked up suddenly and said, "I am a preacher's daughter!"

I tried to cover it by saying, "I am sure you were a great teenager."

As her daughter (and my inner nemesis) was laughing at my embarrassment, she leaned in close and admitted, "I wasn't."

Another time my "cleverness" came back to haunt me was when I was seeing an eighteen-year-old named Abigail for her last well visit. I asked her what her plans were for the future and she told me she was going to be a nurse. She said she already had her CNA certification. Then, she added, "I am going to continue in my training, just like you advised me to do."

I had a proud moment that I had positively influenced this teen's life until she said, "You said to continue getting degrees until I get to the point where I don't have to wipe butts anymore!"

The moment became less proud.

My staff is not afraid to let me know that I am not always as clever as I think I am. On one particularly busy day, my nurse, Amanda, said, "I know your schedule is full, but I have a mom on the phone who thinks her child needs to be seen. Her four-year-old went to the bathroom today and mom saw a worm in his stool."

I continued charting and replied, "Okay" as only a non-listening male can do.

Nonplussed, she continued, "Well, she fished the worm out of the toilet and pushed on it with a popsicle stick."

I looked up, as now this was getting interesting. I asked, "And?"

Happy to have my attention, my nurse excitedly exclaimed, "Green stuff came out of the worm!"

I stared at her, not sure if this was a joke.

"So, should we see the kid?" she asked.

I replied, "The kid? Heck, it sounds like we need to see the worm! He's the one with green stuff coming out of him."

Amanda gave me the disappointed look that I, unfortunately, recognized. She shook her head as if wondering why she took this job.

I quickly replied, "Yes, please put him on the schedule."

One of my biggest pet peeves is when patients miss an entire day of school because they have a well appointment. This happens with all ages but teens are the worst.

Usually, I do not comment on this but on one particular day, the nemesis part of my brain decided it was time to say something.

The patient was a thirteen-year-old female with an appointment at 2:30 p.m. As soon as I walked in the room, her mom announced, "She didn't go to school today so she will need a note."

As I felt my blood pressure start to creep up, I reached for my imaginary soap box. I then began to lecture her about the importance of school and why she should not miss any days unless absolutely necessary.

I was on a pretty good roll when she blurted out, "I had my very first period today."

I froze as if I was a deer staring into headlights. Then, in a very quiet voice I said, "I can get you a note for the rest of the week if you want."

It was one of the few times in my career that a patient has stopped me so abruptly mid-rant. Somewhere, in the deep recesses of my brain, I thought I heard my nemesis laughing.

Fortunately, my big mouth doesn't always get me into trouble. Sometimes, luck is on my side and I stop speaking at just the right time. A few years back I took my young son to see one of the *Star Wars* movies. It just came out and we were very excited to see it. The theater was packed and we got there early to get good seats.

Right before the movie started, a lady walked in with her hair made up to look like Princess Leia. Following behind her were eight little girls obviously there for a birthday party. They proceeded to sit right in front of us. Each had a lightsaber, which they waved during the entire movie.

If that wasn't enough to ruin my experience, the lady also had a small toddler named Henry with her. I know his name was Henry because every five minutes she would say, "Henry, don't put that in your mouth" or "Henry, stop licking the floor."

Needless to say, I left the theater more than a little frustrated.

Fast forward three weeks. I was seeing a mom and her small child when she remarked that she had seen me at the movie theater.

The memory of that day came back to me and I started to angrily tell her about my experience. I was only a few words in when she interrupted me by saying, "I was there with a birthday party for my daughter. I had my hair up like Princess Leia."

I turned to the small toddler sitting on the exam bed . . . Henry! I was just about to put my foot directly into my mouth! I am so glad she interrupted me. I did not recognize her without her cinnamon bun hair. Someone was looking out for me on this one.

Despite the close call above, one of the things I love most about being a doctor in a small town is seeing my patients outside of the office. I see them when I coach youth sports, at restaurants, and at various school functions. It's funny to bump into children in town and watch their amazement when they realize I have a life outside of the clinic.

What is not as cool is the fact that parents still think you are on duty no matter where they see you. When I am off, I want to be a regular dad like everyone else. To stop what I am doing and put on my doctor cap doesn't ruin my day, but it is something I can do without.

I am sure many of you are thinking, "You chose this life when you decided to become a physician."

You are absolutely right and I am sure every profession has its difficulties. I am sure a plumber could complain about all the "crap" they have to deal with. The following two stories both occurred during my "off" time.

It was lunchtime on a Saturday. I pulled into Bojangles for some of my biggest weakness—Bojangles' French fries.

As I was paying the lady at the drive-thru window, she leaned way out and asked, "Are you Dr. Benfield?"

After I confirmed my identity, she said, "Junior is still having his headaches! What do you think we should do?"

This was a valid question. Unfortunately, I had no idea who Junior was. To stall for time, I replied, "If you give me some extra fries, I will make sure we give Junior the best medicine available."

Before I could tell her that I was kidding, she yelled back into the restaurant, "Drop some fries!"

Going to the fair is a huge deal in my town and I usually can count on seeing lots of my patients and their families. Once, when I had first moved to town, I went alone with my four-year-old son. It was a special time for me as this was the first fair when he would be big enough to go on any rides. We were having a great dad/son day.

I was standing at the fence with a goofy, proud look on my face watching him ride the tiny motorcycles when I noticed a woman staring at me. She had three kids with her. Then, I recognized her as being one of my most difficult moms.

This particular mom would call my office once a month with a new request for pain medicine. I would always turn her down but she was relentless and quite imaginative in her requests. I had a baseball hat and sunglasses on and prayed she would not recognize me.

After a few moments, she walked over and asked the dreaded, "Are you Dr. Benfield?"

I kiddingly answered, "No, I am not," and prepared to tell her she could not have pain medicine. Then the oddest thing happened. She believed me!

Before she walked away, she took one more look at me and asked, "Do people ever tell you that you look like him?"

I smiled and replied, "All the time."

As I went to get my son after the ride was over, I felt like a spy who had slipped behind enemy lines. Later, however, I felt guilty. This was no way for a fine, upstanding young physician to behave. I never again lied about my identity.

I simply say, "Yes, I am Dr. Benfield," and prepare for the question that I know is coming.

Another occasion when I tried to mask my identity was when my tractor needed repairs. I knew I had failed in my attempt when a mom asked me during her visit if I had a green tractor. I knew where this was heading, but I told her I did.

She went on to ask, "Were you recently driving it on the road?"

About a week earlier, I had, indeed, driven my tractor about three miles to a repair shop. Given that it was the dead of winter, I had on a big coat, a toboggan, and I added sunglasses so I would not be recognized. I wasn't worried about having to answer patient questions. I literally felt like a knucklehead driving a tractor on a road.

After I admitted to her that she was correct, she exclaimed, "I told my husband that was you and he said, 'Why would Dr. Benfield be driving a tractor on the road?'"

I will admit there are times when patients go too far when asking me questions in public. This was the case when I was recognized at a funeral of one of my chronically ill patients.

This patient was particularly special to me and had lived much longer than anyone thought she would, given her medical condition. The family had asked me to be a pallbearer and shortly after the graveside service ended, I was standing by myself trying to get my emotions under control for a sad goodbye to the child's family.

That's when I heard the often-asked question, "Are you Dr. Benfield?"

This was followed by the just-as-common insistence, "I never do this, but may I ask you a question?"

When I gave the slightest head nod, she went ahead. "My four-year-old is having terrible behavioral problems. He won't listen to anything I say and is constantly having tantrums. What should I do?"

My inner voice suggested I run screaming to the car. But I calmly told her it would be best to bring her son into the office so we could discuss this there.

Given the amount of time I have spent working in the hospital, it is not surprising that some of my worst gaffes have occurred there. Here is an example that occurred on a Saturday morning early in my career.

As part of my hospital rounds, I would perform circumcisions on the male infants whose parents had requested them. This was twenty years ago. During that time, about 99 percent of males underwent this procedure.

On this morning, I had a very full nursery and many inpatients to see before I opened the clinic at 8:30 a.m. Because of how busy it was, one of my partners, Dr. Hayek, came by as I was finishing examining the babies and informed me that he would do all the circumcisions for me.

When he left, he told me he had circumcised all six of the males on the list. I remember thinking that was a high number and wishing Shelby would get a bowling alley so the newborn nursery wouldn't be so full.

The first room I went into was a mom who I knew as I took care of her other child. I had already examined her son in the nursery and told her he looked great. I then mentioned that his circumcision went well.

She looked up alarmed and said, "Please tell me you didn't circumcise my son. My husband is going to be VERY upset."

As this point, I had a mental image of her husband and remembered him being well over six-feet tall and pushing 300 pounds. The next few seconds as we opened that baby's diaper were the longest of my life. I felt so relieved as that uncircumcised penis came into view.

I am not sure if you understand circumcision, but there is no undoing it. Thankfully, Dr. Hayek had properly checked the list and read that this baby was not scheduled for the procedure. Phew! That was a close call!

I had another not-so-shining moment in the hospital nursery a few months later. One of the moms who had just delivered a baby was wanted by the police. Every nurse who came in the nursery reminded me that she was going to be arrested as soon as she was discharged.

When I went in to speak to her, I knew I had to handle this situation with the utmost tact. Therefore, I calmly and nonjudgmentally asked, "Who is going to take care of the baby while you are in jail?"

The father of the baby jumped up but the mom was faster as she came swiftly across the room and started peppering me with questions. "What do you mean while I am in jail!? Am I being arrested? How do you know this?"

Evidently, everyone knew about her pending arrest—*except for her.* I sheepishly went to tell the nurses what I had done. When they went into the room, sure enough, the parents were quickly packing up their stuff. The police had to be called to arrest her right then.

This is not the way to make a positive impression in a new hospital. As I apologized to one of the senior nurses she mused, "Well, you would make one heck of a spy."

Over the next few years, these same nurses would become some of my closest friends. We bonded in our constant battle to make the hospital a better place for children. Pediatrics is not a big moneymaker for a hospital and we would often complain that our floor was lacking amenities that were common on other units.

This complaining came back to haunt me once when a nurse from another floor overheard one of our discussions. The following day, I was seeing a patient in my clinic when my nurse opened the door and announced that the new CEO of the hospital wanted to talk to me. I headed into my office to pick up the phone and found him instead to be sitting there in person.

Like a child in the principal's office, my mind was racing trying to think of what I had done. I was the head of pediatrics at the time, but still found it odd that the CEO was coming to my clinic to talk.

He calmly started with, "I have heard from one of the nurses that you are not happy with how the administration is handling the pediatric floor."

I was honestly confused as I could not remember anything I had recently said to the nurses. I told him I did have concerns about our floor, but could not remember complaining about it.

He then pulled out a small notebook, flipped it open, and read, "They quoted you as saying, 'They treat this floor as if it is a redheaded stepchild!'"

Somewhere, deep in my brain, I definitely heard laughing this time! There was no denying it. That was me. I admitted that I said it and apologized.

Luckily, he was nice about it and was genuinely interested in making pediatrics better. During his time as CEO, we had a good working relationship. I just wished it had started out on a better note.

Sometimes, it feels that even technology is trying to help make me look like a fool. A few years back, my clinic changed over to electronic records. When I started using this system, I would dictate my notes into the chart because I hate to type (I see the irony of that sentence as I type this book).

The dictation software was amazing and recognized almost any medical word I would say. I was also amazed to find that when I dictated the sentence, "The patient has had her first period period," it typed it perfectly instead of typing two dots (periods).

Unfortunately, it did not type many of the phrases I liked to use correctly. Maybe it's because I am Southern but whenever I said something like, "it seems to be" or "it is likely that," the computer would type all kinds of crazy things.

Great. I now had the opportunity to put my foot in my mouth where others could read it. My phone nurses always told me they would read my phone advice once through before reading it aloud to the patients.

More recently, our clinic has a portal where patients can email me their questions directly. Now I had lost my safety net as the patients would be reading exactly what I typed.

Only a few days into this new system I almost made a colossal mistake with a patient who had concerns about her child's diarrhea. The note I dictated to her was supposed to be, "Maybe your child has developed lactose intolerance. Change over to lactofree milk and if the diarrhea stops, then you have your answer."

I was just about to hit send when I read what the computer had typed, "Maybe your child has developed lactose intolerance. Change over to lactofree milk and if the diarrhea stops, then you have CANCER."

Luckily, I caught it before I sent the message. That little man in the computer who types my notes sure does cause me problems. I have sent a requisition to have him replaced by a Southerner.

Even though I like to blame my verbal miscues on the mischievous part of my brain, often my mistakes are simply that my mouth speaks before my brain even gets into gear. The rest of this chapter contains stories of when I begrudgingly admit, I was simply a bit confused.

The first story occurred late one afternoon when I was discussing the future plans of a seventeen-year-old male. He told me he was thinking about going to the University of South Carolina (USC). His mom then told me that he has a brother who is a professor at USC.

She then added, "But they don't know they're brothers."

I was quite surprised by this bombshell and looked at her with a startled look on my face. She had no change in facial expression, so I looked at the patient. He also stared straight ahead like what she said was no big deal.

I leaned in to him and in a quiet voice asked, "You don't know your brother?"

The mom started laughing and said, "He knows his brother! The college doesn't know that they are brothers."

That did make more sense. I was relieved there was not going to be a Jerry Springer moment right in my office.

Sometimes all it takes is a single word to send a normal visit down a very odd path. On this particular morning, I was seeing a newborn of a family that I had not met before. I didn't have any hospital records and was asking for details about the baby's birth.

The mom explained that the baby was born in Bolivia. This made me take a closer look at the mom and dad, both of whom did not look like they came from a foreign country. She explained that their first child was born there and they had such a good experience that they went back for this delivery.

I sat there confused as to why anyone would leave the United States with all our medical technology to go to South America to have a baby. The mom then reported that the baby had a prenatal ultrasound showing enlarged kidneys and had to have a follow-up ultrasound in the hospital.

I said, "Wow. They have ultrasounds in Bolivia."

As I was examining the baby, I noticed he had been circumcised. So, I asked, "They perform circumcisions in Bolivia?"

The parents were now beginning to look at me with an odd look on their faces. I was still perplexed by this whole encounter so I asked, "Were you not nervous about flying to Bolivia while pregnant?"

Dad looked at me like I had a hole in my head and said, "It's only five hours by car."

In case you are as confused as I was, the dad explained to me that Bolivia is a small town just outside of Wilmington, North Carolina. And yes, they have ultrasounds there.

Before you read this story, remember the office can get super busy, so please don't judge. I knew my next visit was with newborn twins but I had not studied their charts and I was over an hour late for the visit.

I walked in the room and both babies were laying on the exam table in only their diapers. They looked to be the same size and I asked, "Are they identical?"

The mom looked at the dad and then replied, "No, one of them is a girl!"

I wanted to walk out the room and ask for a redo. Miraculously, this family continued seeing me.

The dad told me at a later visit that this confusion continued to happen whenever they were out, even when they dressed the female in pink and the male in blue. This really bothered him and he came up with a great reply anytime someone asked him if they were identical. He would reply, "Yes. Except that one has a penis!"

It's not just babies that confuse me. Sometimes teens can do it, too. I was seeing a young teenage male and his brother was sitting in the exam room staring at his phone, ignoring us. The patient was complaining that he didn't have a phone. I suggested, "You don't want to end up like your brother with your face in your phone all the time."

The patient started laughing uncontrollably. His "brother" took off his hat and said, "Hey, I am his SISTER!"

In my defense, she was wearing a baseball hat, had very short hair, and I never got a good look at her face. I really need a time machine that just goes back ten seconds.

Now that I have you questioning my qualification to be a pediatrician, I might as well admit another mistake. When Dermabond first came out to close cuts, my office was one of the first to try it as we all hated using sutures. Dermabond is essentially medical super glue that can be used to close lacerations.

My first experience using it was on a five-year-old female with a small cut on the top of her head. I had watched videos on using this product and I was happy I was going to be able to repair this wound without the little girl experiencing any pain.

I applied the Dermabond and held the cut together with my fingers. After three minutes I said, "Wasn't that easy?" just as I realized my fingers were stuck to the child's head!

Luckily, I had gloves on and so I removed them and then cut the fingers of the glove so that just a tiny amount remained stuck to her head. The parents were very gracious and the little girl thought the whole thing was very funny. I, however, pictured them telling everyone they met that I was responsible for this mess. Her head was a human billboard to my ineptitude.

One aspect of my job that I do not enjoy is filling out forms. Who knew children required so much paperwork? It is mindless work but, as you will see from the story below, it is still important to pay attention.

It was a Friday afternoon and I couldn't go home until I finished the stack of forms on my desk (that may or may not have been sitting there all week). I was filling out a camp form for a child and I noticed in the section that the mom filled out that she had not listed that the child was autistic. She had listed other diagnoses, so I wondered if she didn't want the camp to know.

However, I felt it was important to have this information, so I called mom and asked why she had omitted it.

She replied in a mildly confused tone, "Because it is a camp for autistic children."

I told her that was a good reason and quickly got off the phone. And no, that fact was not listed anywhere on the form.

THINGS THEY DIDN'T TEACH ME IN MEDICAL SCHOOL

I WENT TO MEDICAL SCHOOL AND completed my residency at the University of North Carolina at Chapel Hill. I received an excellent education and, upon graduation, I felt very comfortable that I was ready for whatever pediatrics could throw at me. Boy, was I naive.

The number of situations I have faced over the years where I felt unprepared are mind-boggling. It takes seven years to train a pediatrician, but it takes a lifetime to feel comfortable in the job. That's why they call it "practicing" medicine. This chapter will focus on the times I have felt clueless when confronted with the unexpected craziness that walks into my clinic.

During some of these events, I fully expected Ashton Kutcher to jump out and say, "You just got punked!" like he did after fooling people with silly pranks in the hidden camera television series *Punk'd* that was popular in the 2000s. Practical jokes are probably easier to detect than some of these real-life scenarios!

My first exposure to feeling unprepared to be a physician occurred during my training. In the fall of my internship year (the first year of residency), I had the great opportunity to spend a month practicing pediatrics in Montana. The rotation was on the Crow Indian reservation and the hospital overlooked the site of the Battle of the Little Bighorn. It was a beautiful place and when I arrived, I thought I was going to have the time of my life.

What I didn't know was that the reservation did not have any pediatricians and that I would be in high demand. When the families on the reservation heard about the arrival of a new doc for children, they arrived in droves. The problem was, my medical degree was only two months old and I had not studied very much pediatrics yet. I had two family medicine doctors who were "covering" me but I still saw patients alone. I was told to call them if I had a patient that I didn't know how to handle. My first thought was, *well, that will be all of them!*

I managed fine until my third day when a newborn with an ulcer in his mouth came in. The baby was four days old, accompanied by mom, dad, and grandmother. The mom explained to me that the baby had an ulcer on the bottom of its tongue. The visit was complicated by the fact that the family did not speak English well and my ability to speak the Crow language was, of course, nonexistent.

I examined the baby and was very concerned when I found a distinct yellow ulcer right down the middle of the underside of the baby's tongue. Why was I concerned? Now for the medical lesson: an ulcer in a newborn's mouth can be secondary to the oral herpes virus. In newborns, this virus can infect the brain and cause a potentially deadly infection called encephalitis.

I told the family to wait while I called the family medicine doctor who was covering me. He didn't know much about this virus in newborns and suggested I call a specialist at UNC where I trained. I was able to get an infectious disease specialist on the phone who told me I needed to admit the baby to the hospital, perform a lumbar puncture, and treat the infant with IV antivirals for fourteen days.

This was my third day! I didn't know how to admit a baby to the hospital. I wasn't even sure if legally I could do that since I was a doctor in training.

I anxiously went back in to tell the family the plan. It was difficult with the language barrier but I think they understood the seriousness of the situation. They then translated what I had said to the grandmother.

I was getting up to go make the arrangements when the grandmother motioned to me and put her finger just under her tongue and said something to me in the Crow language. Seeing my confusion, she then took her finger and rubbed the baby's mouth with her finger.

I said, "Yes, I see the ulcer. That is what I am worried about."

She then reached out and took my finger and rubbed the baby's gums with it. I felt something very sharp! I got my flashlight and reexamined the baby's mouth. Just barely visible was a triangularly-shaped tooth peeking through the gum.

There was no herpes infection! This baby had a natal tooth and it had caused the ulcer by rubbing along the bottom of the tongue. Natal teeth are very rare and this one was very sharp. I had been so focused on the ulcer I had missed it. The tooth was so small it was easier to feel than see.

This grandmother had just saved this baby a great deal of trauma and a hospitalization. A dentist happened to be working in the clinic next to mine and came over and filed the tooth smooth in five minutes. The family went home happy.

As for me, I had to call the specialist and tell him about my mistake. I will admit, on this day, I questioned whether I was cut out for this profession. I took solace in the fact that this was a learning experience and I would be ready when I saw this again.

And no, twenty-five years later, I have not seen an ulcer caused by a natal tooth. But I am ready if I do!

Shortly after resuming my training in Chapel Hill, I had another memorable experience with a young child named Curtis. Curtis suffered from a condition called supraventricular tachycardia or SVT, which can cause a child's heart to periodically beat too rapidly. The initial treatment is fairly simple: put cold water or ice on the patient's face, causing them to gasp and take a quick, deep breath in (like when you jump into a cold pool and feel as if your heart has stopped). This "shock" usually will cause the fast rhythm to return to normal.

On the day I met Curtis, I was working in the pediatric emergency room and he came in experiencing SVT. Fortunately, the ice trick worked and he was scheduled to follow up with me in clinic.

During our subsequent visit, his mom asked me what we would do if the ice treatment didn't work. I explained we would have to shock his heart back into rhythm with a defibrillator.

On hearing this, Curtis became scared. He said, "Promise me you will never do that to me."

I told him not to worry; having to shock someone was rarely needed and was always a last resort. Shocking someone, or cardioversion, occurs when doctors put the electrodes on a patient's chest and shock the heart back into rhythm.

And yes, we do yell, "Clear!" just like on television. However, we use a lot less voltage, so the person doesn't dramatically bounce off the table when we are treating SVT. But, truthfully, the idea of shocking anyone made me nervous since I had never done it before.

Fast-forward two weeks and just as my Saturday night shift was ending, Curtis came in again with SVT. This time, his heart had been beating rapidly for more than an hour and he was very lethargic.

We tried using ice with no improvement. We then put in an IV and tried a medicine called adenosine. I kept checking the monitor and his heart rate was still above 200 beats per minute. A normal heart rate for this age child would be between 60 to 100 beats per minute. He was now unconscious and not even responding to stimulation.

My supervising physician brought a defibrillator to the bedside and asked me if I was comfortable cardioverting him with it. I certainly wasn't going to let anyone else treat my patient, but I did feel some guilt, remembering his plea to me about not shocking him.

I placed the paddles on his chest, yelled, "Clear!" and pushed the button. Nothing could have prepared me for what happened next.

Curtis sat straight up with his eyes wide open looking straight at me. He grabbed both of my wrists and then screamed, "You shocked me? You shocked me? I can't believe you shocked me!" And then he fainted and fell back onto the bed.

To this day, I don't know how I didn't soil my pants. He scared me so badly I just stood there, staring as if I was in a trance.

Finally, my supervisor said, "Good job," and pointed to the monitor. His heart rate was back to 110 bpm, and the cardioversion was a success. My heart rate, however, now felt like it was above 200, but I didn't tell anyone ... as I didn't want to be shocked either!

Right after joining the Shelby Children's Clinic, I began taking call shifts at the local hospital. It was immediately obvious that I needed to learn new ways to communicate with the hospital staff.

When I was training, if I ordered a lab or x-ray "stat" I could count on my urgent request occurring between one to four hours later. However, in a small hospital, I learned that people take this term much more seriously.

For example, I was seeing a child in the pediatric unit who had developed a bad cough after having his appendix removed. I wanted to see his x-ray before I headed over to the clinic so I told the nurse I wanted the film ordered stat. Less than five minutes later, I heard two people running up the hall pushing a portable x-ray machine.

Out of breath, one of them looked at me and exclaimed, "We are here to do the stat x-ray!"

Unfortunately, I repeated this mistake one other time when, out of habit, I ordered a stat blood culture on a child with fever. This time the phlebotomist (person who draws blood) showed up with food on his face and explained to the nurse that he was eating his lunch when the stat call came through.

As part of the on-call responsibilities for my practice, I was in charge of our hospital's newborn nursery. This was a unique experience. Early each morning, I would show up to a room filled with anywhere from four to fourteen newborns. I would then go down the line examining each baby and making notes about each one on a piece of paper.

During my first few months, if I came to a baby with a dirty diaper, I would quickly change it. However, after showing up late at the clinic a few times on my on-call days, I abandoned this task to save time. On the day I stopped doing diaper duty, I heard one nurse say to another, "Four months! He made it longer than we thought he would!"

Evidently, they had taken bets to see how long I would continue with the diaper changes.

After examining the babies, I would visit each room to talk to their parents. I enjoyed teaching parents about their babies, especially first-time parents as everything I was telling them was brand new and they listened very intently.

These rounds were a bit hectic because I had to complete them and be in the clinic by 9:30 a.m. One morning, I went in to see a mom of a newborn and as I walked into the room, I could see the mom was asleep in the bed.

I needed to be at the clinic soon, so I decided to wake her up. As I walked further into the room, I quickly noticed that the mom was laying facing away from me and did not have a top on. Then, I noticed she also had a shaved head.

Thoughts ran through my brain. *Do I go get the nurse? Should I call her on the phone later? Why doesn't she have any hair?*

At that moment, as if sensing my presence, she began rolling over. I wanted to look down to preserve her dignity, but curiosity won and I witnessed a very pale, large, body roll over to face me with parts jiggling everywhere. Her face also shocked me as it looked like she had a five o'clock shadow.

I literally stood there frozen, unable to speak when "she" said, "My wife is in the shower."

He actually pronounced it "shire" but I knew what he meant. This was no pregnant lady! It was her pale, obese, hairless husband! Some people have nightmares about monsters, but I wake up in a sweat picturing him turning over in that bed (usually in slow motion).

The hospital was also the location of one of my most embarrassing moments as a physician. This event was so damaging that I asked the nurses to never put patients of mine in the room where this occurred again.

So, what happened in dreaded Room Number 13? Only for the sake of this book will I revisit this emotionally-scarring event.

It was a beautiful Saturday afternoon and I was on call and making rounds at the hospital. There was a two-year-old child with pneumonia who had just been admitted to the hospital and I went into Room Number 13 to take the history from the parents. The child had a complicated medical past so obtaining all the information I needed took almost half an hour.

I was finally ready to examine the child. I washed my hands in the sink by the bed and reached for a paper towel. As fate (or possibly karma) would have it, the paper towel dispenser was empty.

Knowing there were more in the bathroom, I pushed down the handle with my elbow and opened the door firmly with my foot. Sitting and facing me on the toilet was grandma!

She had a horrified look on her face and let out a tiny squeal.

My acrobatic entrance had swung the door all the way open, meaning I had to step fully into the bathroom to close it again, all the while saying, "Sorry. So sorry!"

I was in that patient's room *for almost thirty minutes.* Never for a second did I think there could be anyone in that bathroom. As years passed, every time I would go back into Room Number 13, I would have flashbacks of that fateful day. I just hope the shocked lady didn't have flashbacks every time she sat down to do her business.

Shortly after I arrived in Shelby, I learned that communication with the nurses and staff in my clinic was going to be very important as well. During my training, the nursing staff were familiar with young doctors in training and basically tolerated us. The staff in my office quickly became my work friends and this led to a very different dynamic.

In training, you are expected to tell a nurse to do something. In private practice, you ask your "friend" if they would mind doing something for you. This was not difficult for me as my clinic has been blessed with an awesome staff.

However, that doesn't mean communication errors do not occur. Once, I sent my nurse a note on the computer saying, "Please read this patient's x-ray to his mom."

The x-ray was of a patient's leg and the radiologist had written in the accompanying notes that there was no fracture. The nurse was waiting for me when I came out of the room. She told me, "I don't feel comfortable calling that mom."

When I asked why not, she replied, "I have never 'read' an x-ray before. I really don't know how."

She was very relieved when I explained that I just wanted her to read the radiologist's report and not actually interpret the x-ray.

Another big miscommunication occurred one fateful day at the clinic when the word "sat" was misunderstood. I was having lunch when an administrator from the company I work for called wanting to speak to me immediately about an injury to a baby in my clinic. She was a bit upset and it took me quite some time to understand her concern.

Evidently the day before, we had a baby who was having trouble breathing. We had checked an oxygen saturation level or an "O2 sat" on the baby. My nurse called administration to tell them that our pulse oximeter was malfunctioning and we needed a new one. She went on to explain that we had to send the baby to the emergency room to get an O2 sat.

She left this on a voicemail but by the time the story reached this upper-level administrator it had changed to, "the baby had to be sent to the emergency room because one of the staff had "sat" on them!"

She was very relieved when I explained what had truly happened. However, she told me she was taking the rest of the day off because her nerves were shot.

One of our nurses' hardest jobs is getting the pronunciation of our patients' names right. This is key because the nurse has to call for the patient in a busy waiting room. Butchering the name is not only embarrassing, it usually makes the parents angry.

I was seeing a child named Malachi and when my previous nurse went out to get him out of the waiting room, she called him "Maleeky."

I'm sure the parent did not think it was funny, but that wasn't the worst part. The problem is this child's last name is Johnson. Not only did she call him Maleeky, she called out in front of everybody in the waiting room, "Maleeky Johnson, it's your turn, Maleeky Johnson."

She said many of the parents laughed and she didn't understand why until I explained it to her. Call me if you need me to explain it to you.

This was not this nurse's only embarrassing waiting room experience as she was notorious for incorrectly calling names. She went to a very full waiting room one time and called for "Jesus."

A few people laughed and everyone waited to see who would stand up. I am sure some felt they had chosen an excellent practice if Jesus was a patient here.

Finally, a young Hispanic mom walked up with her small son hiding behind her. We call him "Heh-soos," she told my very embarrassed nurse.

In a fiction book this would be the end of the story. However, life is often funnier than fiction. Only a few weeks later, my nurse was walking to the waiting room to get another child named Jesus.

This time she correctly pronounced it and looked across the room at a Hispanic family. When no one stood up, she stared right at the Hispanic family and loudly repeated "Heh-soos."

The Hispanic family looked at each other nervously and then shrugged their shoulders.

Again, no one stood up. The nurse quietly called out, "Jesus?"

Now, everyone in the waiting room was either giggling or whispering to each other, so my nurse tried once more but this time just said the baby's last name.

A mom hesitantly stood up with her newborn and said, "I think you mean us."

My nurse looked at the tiny, light-skinned newborn wrapped in pink and said, "No, I don't think so."

The mom looked at the paper in my nurse's hand and pointed to the name saying, "This says 'Josie' not Jesus."

My nurse was mortified. But the mom and I had a good laugh about it. Josie is now six years old and every time I see her, I call her Heh-soos.

I think now would be a good time to bring up any pediatrician's favorite subject: children with interesting names. When I get together with other pediatricians or teachers, there is typically a competition about who has seen the patients with the most unusual names. The contest is usually over when I report that I once took care of a newborn named Lucifer (this is a name in the book that I did not change).

I first met Lucifer at his newborn well check and was surprised not only by his name but also his middle name: Morning Star.

I was Lucifer's dad's pediatrician when he was a child and so felt comfortable asking him why he named the baby this.

He explained that Lucifer also means "the light" and added that the original Lucifer was an angel before he became the devil.

He was right, but I worry about the reactions this child will receive for the rest of his life.

Many of my patients with unusual names love the fact that their name makes them unique and do not mind the attention it brings. However, I worry that some names such as this next one would be hard to live with.

I first heard this person's name when they came for a newborn well check and Amanda, my nurse at the time, asked me to help her pronounce it before she called for them in the waiting room.

The name in the chart was Tdquilla and I told Amanda I was not sure and to call the baby by the last name.

When Amanda came out of the room she said, the "d" is silent and so the name is pronounced "Tequila."

I was shocked and then she added, "And her middle name is 'Margarita'"!

I shook my head at her joke and said, "Ha-ha, very funny."

She then put the chart in front of me and, sure enough, that was the child's middle name.

Sometimes, instead of letters being silent in names, imaginative parents want them pronounced. This became clear one summer morning when I met a little girl for the first time named Na-wa.

I walked into the room and said, "Hi Na-wa. It is nice to meet you."

The mom corrected me, "Her name is pronounced 'Nadashwa.'"

I stared at her with a confused look on my face and so after a deep sigh she explained, "The dash is not silent."

I have another patient with a name that appears difficult to say, but is really quite simple once you get the hang of it. I met Phithamae in the newborn nursery. When I met her mom, I asked her to pronounce her baby's name for me.

She replied, "Fifth-a-may."

She added, "I was watching TV when I was pregnant with her and the newscaster said, "Tomorrow is the fifth of May," and I liked the way it sounded. So, I named her that."

As this child became older, she went by the name Mae, which I loved, and I usually called her "Mae Mae" during our visits.

Mae once told me that she loved her name except for the first day of school when all the teachers would call her "Phith-Amy" when taking roll.

Mae has a sister named September. I once encouraged her mom to have twelve children so we could get all the months covered but she quickly declined.

Mae was one of my favorite patients and even shadowed me for clinical experience when she was in high school and curious about working in the medical field. Sadly, she is now in her twenties and has aged out of my practice. But I still occasionally see her when she brings her younger siblings.

I was discussing unique names with a dad when he told me that his five-year-old came home after the first week of school and reported that there was a child in her class named Internet.

The dad said he felt naming your child Internet should be considered child abuse and was quite upset about it.

He went on to tell me that he felt better when he went to school to eat lunch with his daughter and met the infamous child.

He asked her what her name was and she replied sweetly, "I'm Antoinette."

One of the best stories about a name came when I was seeing a newborn named Henry Beam V. I commented to the baby's dad that I had not seen many "fifths" in my career.

He smiled and proudly said, "Yes, this is our little 'Fifth of Beam!'"

It took me a minute to stop laughing at this ingenious dad joke.

On another occasion, I met a baby who also had the last name Beam, first name Navey. I loved this combination, but my nurse did not get it as she had never heard of a navy bean.

I had one of my famous "foot in mouth" experiences when I was seeing a five-year-old girl named Betty for a cough. I noticed in the chart that her middle name was Elizabeth and knowing that Betty is one of the many ways that the name Elizabeth can be shortened, I started calling her Betty Betty.

At the end of the visit, the mom asked, "Why are you calling her that?"

I explained my reasoning and she cocked her head and said, "Are you telling me I named my child Betty Betty?"

After a long silence, I meekly said, "Yes, but I do not think most people will realize this."

Betty, however, loved it. She was bouncing around the room saying, "Betty Betty! I'm Betty Betty!"

In order to be a pediatrician, a person must go to four years of college, followed by four years of medical school, then three years of residency. You would think that after all that training, I would be prepared for anything. You would be wrong.

I was having a typical summer afternoon at the clinic when I went into what I imagined would be a routine visit with a thirteen-year-old male named Dixon. According to the chart, Dixon was coming in with a concussion. I walked in to see him sitting on the table wearing sunglasses and obviously not feeling well.

I started with my usual, "So, tell me how you were injured?"

Dixon looked up and replied in a monotone voice, "A rooster did it."

My mind quickly went through all the possibilities in this scenario. I settled on the most likely and asked, "You hit your head while being attacked by a rooster?"

Dixon shook his head and replied, "No. The rooster hit me in the head."

I now pictured a rooster pecking him repeatedly, like Woody Woodpecker. I began to doubt that Dixon had a concussion after all. I tried to shake this humorous mental image and asked in as serious a tone as I could, "A rooster pecked you in the head?"

The mom now interjected, "It didn't peck him. It chased him and when he fell to the ground it spurred him multiple times on the back of his head. We had to go to the emergency room last night." She pulled his hair aside to show me three shallow lacerations in his hairline. "The emergency room doctor glued his cuts back together and told us he had a concussion," she explained.

(If you have never been faced with an angry rooster, "spurring" is when a rooster hits you with a large claw called a spur that is located on the back of its leg.)

I held in my inner sarcastic thought. *Well, if the ER said it, it must be true.* Instead, I verbalized, "I am not sure a rooster can hit you with enough force to cause a concussion, but let's take a look at you."

I then put Dixon through my bedside testing for a concussion and it was quite abnormal. His balance was off, he had trouble with simple mental tasks, and his eyes had a twitch when he was tracking my finger, a condition we call nystagmus. All these symptoms are present when someone has a concussion.

I admitted to Dixon and his mom that I was wrong. It did appear that a rooster could give you a concussion after all.

Dixon agreed by saying, "It felt like I was being kicked in the head with a boot."

Later, I scolded myself for jumping to conclusions and not remembering the golden rules: *Always listen to your patient. Never make assumptions before finishing the exam.*

Those are great guiding principles, for sure. But somehow, *never mess with an angry rooster* is what stuck with me instead.

When taking care of children, it has always amazed me how fast a routine visit can go south. Children are certainly unpredictable, but often it is the adults who shock me.

On this occasion, I was midway through a well visit when I noticed the newborn baby had an accessory nipple. I have a standard approach to this. First, I explain it to the mom, then I tell her never to mention it again. I don't want the child to be self-conscious about it and I also worry they will tell a friend and then be made fun of during middle school if others found out.

I told the mom, "You see this little birthmark right here below your child's nipple, that's called an accessory nipple. They usually fade over time and won't look like a nipple when he is older."

The mom nodded and seemed to accept this information without too much emotion. But the baby's aunt, who was also at the visit, decided she would have a different response. The aunt, who likely weighed more than 250 pounds, immediately started pulling her shirt up.

I quickly said, "Whoa, whoa! What are you doing?"

She replied, "Well, I was going to show you that mine never changed. It still looks just like a nipple!"

If you have read this far in the book, you have realized that I seem to be a magnet for funny and odd situations. When I tell stories at work, my partners often say, "Why does stuff like this always happen to you?"

The following story is a great example of my magnetic ability. I was seeing a patient with a cold when his mom asked me about her other child's rash.

The child wasn't there but mom had pictures and she showed them to me on her phone. She handed me the phone and I told her I couldn't tell what the rash was from the picture. She said there were more pictures so I swiped through four or five more. Then, I swiped one too far!

The picture I stopped at was a drawing of a sexual position with the heading, "The Banana Split." Underneath the picture were six steps of instructions for this position.

I remember thinking that any position with that many steps would likely be hard for me to remember how to do. Plus, stopping midway to get my reading glasses to check the list would surely ruin the mood!

Back to the story. I quickly closed the phone and told the mom that the rash looked like eczema and told her what cream would help.

Since then, when anyone hands me a phone to look at pictures I can feel my blood pressure go up. I have "embarrassing picture PTSD" and never swipe past the picture someone is showing me.

Traditionally, when an infant is born, someone in the family (usually a grandparent) will ask if they have all their fingers and toes. On one memorable visit, I was seeing a newborn. The baby had six fingers on each hand and six toes on each foot. I told mom that was rare but that I had seen it before.

Surprisingly, she replied, "Yeah, I had the same thing."

She went on to say, in a very thick Southern accent, "But the durn doctor removed the wrong toe."

"What do you mean he removed the wrong toe?"

She pulled off her shoe and showed me that, sure enough, he had taken off the toe that connected to a joint and had left the toe that wasn't connected to a joint, so it was just kind of flapping in the breeze.

As I was getting over my shock, the baby's dad added, "Do you think we can still sue for that?"

Fast-forward one year and the same mom came into my office with a new baby. It had been a while since I had seen her and I didn't even know she was pregnant. I walked in and I said, "Well, my goodness, you had another baby."

And the daddy said, "Yep! And things are getting better."

I didn't understand and asked, "What do you mean? What's getting better?"

He replied, "Well, our other baby had six fingers on each hand and six toes on each foot. But this baby here, he's got six fingers on each hand and six toes on his right foot, but on his left foot he's got FIVE toes! It's getting better!"

How can you argue with that logic?

One of the things I learned very early in my career is that children like to hug. When you are having a bad day, being squeezed by a child makes everything instantly better. However, I had one visit where that was not the case.

I had just finished performing a well check on a three-year-old named Sonya when she yelled, "I need a hug, I need a hug, I need a hug!"

She jumped into my lap and I gave her a big head-to-head hug, squeezing her tight. She was still on my lap when her mom said, "Oh yeah, I have another question about her. I just treated her for lice two days ago and I'm still seeing nits in her hair. What else should I do?"

You should now have a mental image of me running out of the room screaming. But, remember! I am a professional. I calmly answered the question, buying time while waiting for Ashton to appear to tell me I had been punked. When he didn't appear, I ran out of the office screaming!

Another aspect about being a doctor that I like is that I never know what I will see when I open the door and go into a room. Like the time I walked in to see my nurse standing by the sink and a four-year-old male was sitting on the bed with not a stitch of clothes on.

This boy had his hands covering his privates and was obviously incredibly embarrassed. As I stood there very confused, my nurse explained that the child had vomited all over his clothes and his mom went to the car to find him something to wear.

It was my nurse's turn to be embarrassed when I reminded her we had gowns for patients to wear in the cabinet behind her.

Speaking of gowns, we know patients hate to wear them and I usually only use them for teens during well visits. On one memorable occasion my partner, Dr. Hendrix, was seeing a male teen and walked in to find him sitting on the bed totally nude with his gown—still folded in a tiny square—covering his privates.

She quickly explained to him that he was supposed to *wear* the gown.

The teen was mortified and admitted that he was confused when the nurse told him to get undressed and cover yourself with the gown.

I am sure every job has its share of unexpected moments but I feel being a pediatrician is near the top for the most outrageous. Take, for example, the phone call I received from a mom of a two-year-old named Brooks.

"My child has a habit of chewing on an Afghan rug in our living room," she began. "The rug has these little strings that kind of hang off of it and Brooks spends a lot of time chewing on them."

I remember thinking, *why do you let him do that?* But only replied, "Okay."

Mom went on to say, "We never really thought anything about it until yesterday when he threw up some string. Should we get an x-ray?"

I reassured her that he must have swallowed a small piece of fringe and that an x-ray was not necessary as string would not show up on an x-ray.

She replied, "Well, we were just worried because it was a large ball of string about the size of a baseball."

I laughed nervously and said, "Are you serious?"

It turns out they were serious. An hour later, I got to meet Brooks in my office along with a disgusting baseball-sized wad of string. Brooks did get his x-ray to prove he did not have an obstruction. The film was normal and Brooks was allowed to go home and eat a soft diet for a few days.

As his mom was leaving, she said, "Don't worry, Dr. Benfield, we will throw away that rug!"

Throw away the rug. Watch your child a little more closely. Your choice.

Luckily, this time I just thought about saying it and kept my mouth shut.

Sometimes, the odd things that happen in my office are difficult to explain, but I'll take a stab at it here. One Monday morning, I was seeing a baby for a well visit and her brother was there as well. The brother was about four years old and he put the H in ADHD.

This child was running around the small exam room alternating between climbing on the exam table and jumping off a chair. I didn't think I was this child's doctor as I didn't recognize him and he was very memorable.

He then decided to pull on my lab coat and repeat over and over, "You don't know my name, you don't know my name."

I looked him right in the eyes and said, "Of course, I do. It's Jeremy."

He stopped and stared at me and then looked at his mom and said, "How did he know my name was Jeremy?"

She replied, "He's a doctor. He's probably seen you before."

Well, in all honesty, I made up the name Jeremy just to be funny. I didn't remember this kid and I certainly didn't know his name. It was just the first name that popped into my head.

Either I have supreme ESP or this is one of the biggest coincidences ever. Cue the *Twilight Zone* music.

This last story is included to reiterate, "There is no way medical school can prepare you for the myriad things a physician will see when they walk into an exam room." The source of my amazement on this particular day was a four-year-old child named Steven who came to the clinic to see me because of "an injury to his penis."

Unfortunately, for the male population, this is not an uncommon reason for a visit. What made this one different was the way the injury occurred.

Stephen's mom reported that when he was taking a nap at daycare another child bit him on the penis! He had been wearing jeans but the child bit him hard enough to leave teeth marks in the skin. *Why would a child do this?* Luckily, he was an easygoing kid and did not seem to have any psychological trauma from this event.

Interestingly, I was seeing Stephen in my office some thirteen years later. I told him I was writing a book about my experiences being a pediatrician.

He asked, "Am I in the book?"

I gave him a wry smile (at least I think that is what I tried to express). He screamed, "Not the penis story!"

Sorry, Stephen.

TRICKS OF THE TRADE

Over the years, I have developed many techniques to make my job easier. Kids are squirmy little creatures and it takes a lot of tricks to hold their attention and keep them happy. I have also found that children are often very nervous during their visits and making them laugh can help them relax.

I must admit this is not the only purpose for my jokes. I enjoy cutting up with children and teasing them. This is one of the main reasons I became a pediatrician. I cannot imagine taking care of adults. I need an audience that enjoys potty humor as much as I do.

Now, I will let you in on some of my tricks that keep children relaxed and me entertained during a visit.

For most patients, the physical exam is the part of the visit that makes them the most nervous. As I stand up and walk toward them, I often notice them starting to fidget with their hands. With younger children, I can distract them with something in my pocket or by asking about their pets.

When I am dealing with older patients, I will often begin by saying, "I want to teach you how to be a doctor. So, what body part does a doctor always start with?"

About 70 percent of my patients guess the correct answer by saying the heart.

I then reply, "Doctors always start with the heart."

I then pause before adding, "Because if that is not beating … I'm done! I just go to the next room. It's a real time saver!"

This usually gets a good laugh although, occasionally, neither the patient nor the parent gets the joke so I move on quickly.

My worst experience with this attempt at humor was when a fifteen-year-old male broke down in tears after hearing this! I quickly reassured him that his heart was not going to stop and his mother added, "He is very sensitive."

I made a quick mental note not to play jokes on him in the future.

Then there was the teenage girl who had an interesting response to the question, "What does a doctor start with?"

She thought about it and then replied, "D?"

She was not wrong.

This joke also misfired when I had a seven-year-old reply to it by saying, "Well, maybe I am a zombie."

I replied that zombies' hearts are still beating—it's their brain that is malfunctioning. This led to a passionate argument between us which went on a bit too long. The mom had to clear her throat to remind me that they were here for a well check and we should get on with it.

I wanted to call this little boy later so I could win the argument but I was afraid I might end up being discussed on Facebook.

While listening to a patient's heart, I will often comment on their heart rate. A slow resting heart rate often means the child is getting plenty of exercise. I will praise the older kids and encourage them to keep exercising.

When I hear a fast heart rate in a teen male, I will tell them that they have a "*Fortnite* heart rate" and they need to stop playing so many video games.

The teen girls with rapid heart rates usually hear, "Your heart rate tells me that you are not exercising much. I want you to visit this new place. It's called outside!"

My standard line when I hear a slow heart rate in a small child is, "Man, you have a great heart rate! You must run around like a chicken all day." I find it interesting that of all my funny sayings, this simple phrase gets a laugh more frequently than anything else I say.

Next, I move on the lungs. If the child is there for a well check, I have many ways of joking around with them during this part of the exam. If the child is between ages five and twelve, I like to tell them their lungs sound so much better since they stopped smoking. As they laugh and deny this, it gives the parent and me an opportunity to remind them that this is a habit that we never want them to try.

Early in my career, I was examining a teen female and as I leaned in to listen to her lungs, I smelled smoke. I then asked her if she smoked.

She replied a bit alarmed, "I do. Why? Do you hear something in my lungs?"

I really wanted her to stop smoking so maybe I stretched the truth a bit. "Yes, your lungs don't sound that great. You really need to give up the cigarettes."

Don't judge me. The next time I saw her she told me she had quit and I believe, in this case, the end justifies the means.

Another entertaining part of the lung exam is watching kindergarten and preschool children trying to take deep breaths. They are very dramatic and usually add verbal huffing noises like the big bad wolf. Sometimes I will start with the lungs and when I move on to the heart I tell them, "Okay, now you can breathe normally."

The children frequently open their eyes wide and start struggling to breathe. No one has ever told them how to breathe normally and they truly are not sure how to do it!

The most challenging part of a physical exam is checking the child's ears, especially when the patient is a toddler. Ask any pediatrician what age is the most difficult to examine and they will all answer toddlers. This age is difficult because they often have stranger anxiety and cry during the exam.

Therefore, when examining a toddler, it helps to approach them slowly and—as odd as it may sound—not make eye contact while you are checking them. I have often found that if I whisper something very quietly as I check their ears, it will make many of them hold still as they try to hear me.

The other key with this age group is having a mom who is a good holder for the children that want to fight while we check their mouths or ears. First-time moms usually feel guilty and are not the best at this. I like an experienced mom. They will put the toddler in a great headlock as soon as they see you get the otoscope out.

I recently had a reminder of how difficult it is to hold a child when a twenty-month-old was in the office who needed to be checked for Covid. His mom had just had surgery and so was unable to hold him. I volunteered to do it while my nurse performed the test.

I sat him on my lap and held him exactly like I showed my parents, but it took almost three minutes to do the test. He was like Houdini and kept escaping my arms. At one point, he climbed up my body and was almost sitting on my head. My nurse stated that next time she would get one of the other nurses to hold the child.

Examining older kids is much easier but there are still challenges. Kids aged three to seven do not usually cry during the examination, but they still do not like their ears checked. Our trick with this age group is simply to tell them we are looking for something in their ear.

Over the years, I have looked for animals, dinosaurs, trains, Barney, Spider-Man, Elsa, and most recently, Paw Patrol in children's ears. It is such a silly thing to do, but the kids seem to love it when I announce what or who I see when I am looking.

Recently, after announcing that I saw Batman in a four-year-old boy's ear, he replied, "Mom, you didn't get Batman out last night when you cleaned my ears?"

Occasionally, I really will find things in children's ears. I have seen erasers, toys, paper, the end of Q-tips, and even food. On a side note, I have noticed that in the last few years I am seeing less foreign bodies in children's ears and noses. My theory is that because children spend so much time on tablets and phones, they are less bored than in the past. Therefore, they don't feel the need to entertain themselves by sticking things in their various orifices. So, there is at least one good thing to come from this new technology.

One of my worst ear discoveries came when I was examining a very anxious eight-year-old male named Trevor. He was a frequent visitor to my clinic as his anxiety made him hyperaware of his body. He often came in so I could reassure him that his latest symptom was not anything to worry about.

His complaint on this visit was that he felt something moving in his ear. As I was getting ready to examine him, I jokingly said, "I better not see a bug in here."

His eyes widened and he said, "Are you serious? Could there be a bug in there?"

Inwardly chastising myself for my poor tact, I replied, "No, of course not. You are just likely feeling some wax."

I then looked into his ear canal and found myself face-to-face with a live bug. It was small but looked huge with my magnified otoscope.

My instinct was to run from the room screaming but remembering my earlier mistake I calmly said, "Yep. Just a bit of wax. I need to get a little bit of water to flush it out."

I then put a few drops of rubbing alcohol in his ear canal to kill the bug and after waiting a few minutes removed it with a specialized pair of tweezers.

Trevor of course wanted to see the "wax," but I told him it was too disgusting and quickly threw it away. He is in his late teens now and I still see him often. I have not, and will not, tell him what I pulled out of his ear on that fateful day. *Please do not tell him either!*

Checking the ears of older children is an opportunity for joking with them. I often will tell them I can see their brain and then add, "Well, that is interesting!" When they ask what I see, I report seeing an empty walnut shell, or a tiny pea, or a sign that says, "No one is home."

When they have siblings present, I like to look in one of the children's ears and tell them I can see their sibling sitting beside them. It never ceases to amaze me how often the sibling will look into the other ear and wave!

We now move on to the part of the exam for which I am most famous. I know what you are thinking: *how can someone be famous for part of an exam?* The answer is years of practice!

It is not unusual when a patient sees me in the hall to ask, "Is that Dr. Nose?" or "Is he the one with the nose?"

Let me explain. About fifteen years ago, a drug rep gave me a very authentic-looking rubber nose with the word Flonase written across it. It was filled with a clear, glue-like substance that would come out of each nose hole about a half an inch when you squeezed it.

After removing the logo with rubbing alcohol, I now had my favorite toy. During visits, I keep it in my pocket until it is time for the trick and then I hide it in my hand. I then say, "Let's have a look at your nose" as I pretend to take their nose from their face.

At this point, most young kids are interested in how this is going to turn out. Older kids give me an unimpressed, "I am too cool for this" look.

Then, like a magician, I push the nose up through my fingers and squeeze it saying, "Man, you are snotty!"

The older kids are now very flummoxed and do a double take or stutter a reply. This nose looks very real and even though the teens know that it's fake, most will nonchalantly reach up and touch their nose. They don't think I see them, but I am watching for it. It is part of what makes me enjoy the trick.

As for the response of the younger kids, it depends on their age. I learned very early that this was not a trick for the five-and-under crowd. They take this very seriously and usually end up crying or under the table.

I also have to be careful with the six- to eight-year-old age group. I usually tell them, "It says in your chart that you have two noses. One in the front and one in the back."

As they are denying this, I "pull" the fake nose off the back of their head and show it to them. They always rub the back of their head laughing or saying "What!?"

Children aged nine to thirteen love this trick the most. They always want to hold the nose and squeeze the snot out themselves. The boys usually want to touch the "snot."

Whenever a patient comes in who I have seen many times, I often watch them staring at my hands to see if they can catch me doing the trick. With these kids, I find the nose in an unexpected place, like on their knee or behind their ear.

Who would have thought that a gift from a drug rep could bring so much joy?

As I have mentioned earlier, my trick when examining a child's abdomen is to try to guess what they had for breakfast or lunch. The thing I like best about this routine is that the youngest kids will usually say I am right no matter what I guess. This has also taught me the sad fact that too many children skip breakfast.

Once, when I was examining an infant's abdomen, they passed very loud gas. I told the mom and grandmother I was sorry but I had accidentally pushed the gas button on the baby.

Instead of laughing, the grandmother jumped up and said, "Show me! She has so much gas. I need to know where to push!"

The next part of the exam is the "privates" and I devoted an entire chapter to the male variety of this part. As for the females, I do not joke about this part very often but I did have one young lady put me in my place about it.

She jumped up on the table and pointed her finger at me, declaring, "You're not going to check my bathing suit area, are you?"

I stole that term from her and used it for my future patients, who seemed to like the description better than "privates."

After I finish examining a patient, I usually stop joking around while the parents and I discuss my assessment and plan. I will admit, however, that there is one joke I cannot resist telling.

When a child needs an antibiotic, I often use one called Omnicef. I like this one because it tastes good and only needs to be given one time per day. It does, however, have one side effect that can be very concerning to parents. It is a white-colored liquid but it is actually strawberry-banana flavored. In some children, the strawberry coloring shows up in the stool and looks a lot like blood.

I have even had moms bring in their baby's diaper saying, "I know you warned me about this but I think this is indeed blood."

The first couple of times I was fooled as well and tested the stool in our lab only to find that there was no blood, just red dye.

Each time I prescribe Omnicef, I warn the mom and the patient about this possible issue. If the child is old enough, I will look at them, "So, if you look in the potty and see red poo, don't call me. But if you look in the potty and see Winnie the Pooh ... call me immediately!"

I will admit that many kids today do not know this character but the parents still like the joke.

Being a male pediatrician, I not only tell dad jokes, I tell doctor dad jokes. One of my favorites is whenever a patient comes in with a stomach bug, I will say, "Did you know diarrhea is genetic? It runs in your jeans!"

However, I learned I have to deliver the punchline quickly with this joke.

On one occasion, I said the first part to a teenager and his grandmother interjected, "Oh no! I am so sorry I have given you my chronic diarrhea."

It was then not as funny to explain the joke to the mortified teen.

At the end of the visit in my clinic, each patient leaves with a sticker or two. This is a powerful tool as often a parent will say during the visit, "If you aren't good, he will not give you a sticker."

I will occasionally not give stickers when a child acts up but, in these cases, will give them to the parent and tell the child that their parent will give them the stickers when they start listening better.

On one very memorable occasion, I took a sticker back from a child. She was a five-year-old female and I had given her a sticker after doing a strep test. When I returned to tell the family the results the child was standing on my desk.

I knew this child well and had been caring for her and her sister for many years. Unfortunately, this child had rarely been disciplined. That day, her mom was looking at her phone and didn't seem to care that her child was standing on my desk.

I was shocked as I had never had a patient do this before and told her to get down. She looked at me and screamed, "No!"

Feeling like this was a great time to model parenting techniques for this mom, I reached up and pulled the child's sticker off her shirt and said, "Okay. That means no sticker."

The child immediately jumped down and said, "I'm sorry. Please can I have my sticker?"

I looked to the mom to make sure she was seeing all this great teaching. She had never looked up. Eyes still locked on the phone.

I did, however, make a big impression on the child. For years after that she behaved very well during her visits and once said in a sad voice, "You're not going to take my sticker away again, are you?"

This story reminded me of another child who had never heard the word "No." He was a very cute but poorly behaved four-year-old. I was seeing him for a sick visit and I asked his mother how he tolerated the vaccines that he had received two weeks earlier.

She said he did well, but wouldn't let them remove the bandage that was placed on his arm after receiving the shots.

I lifted his shirt to find a dirty, disgusting band aid that was practically disintegrating on his arm.

Mom shrugged her shoulders and said, "He says we can't touch it."

I grabbed the end of that band aid and quickly ripped it off his arm.

The look on his face was one of extreme shock. He could not believe someone had done something against his will. I gently told the mom, "You are the mom. He is the child. You are in charge."

It is during times like this that I feel very helpless. This mom needed so much guidance. But I only see children a few times each year which is not nearly enough time to make a significant difference in parenting skills.

Let me get back to the stickers. After twenty-three years of handing out stickers, I can usually guess what sticker a child is going to pick. After a while, I turned this into a game.

Typically, I will have up to 100 stickers in my pocket. Sticker packets come in sets of five so there are lots of "repeats." I like to carry about six or seven different "types" of stickers, like Batman and Dora, so I have something for every age and gender.

I always have *Frozen* stickers as I can guarantee most girls under age eight will pick those. One time, we were out of them and my five-year-old patient was very unhappy. While she was waiting for her lab results, I put a Barbie sticker in the freezer. After I had her labs, I walked back into the room and said, "Here is your "frozen" sticker." She did not think it was funny.

Each physician picks out their stickers from a catalog each month. I often have to be reminded by my nurse that I have female patients too. I find myself only picking out stickers that I like.

At the end of the visit, I often announce to the patient that I have a magic trick for them. I pick a copy of the sticker that I think they will choose and set it face down on my desk. I then show them all the stickers making sure to briefly pause on the one I want them to pick. I will say they pick that sticker 75 percent of the time.

I then say "abracadabra" and tap the sticker on my desk before showing it to them. When I am right, they are speechless and usually ask their mom to explain how I did that.

I have been doing this trick for so long that many of my patients start getting excited at sticker time saying, "You are not going to guess what I am going to pick today!"

Some of my patients who don't like "losing" will intentionally pick something unexpected just to prove me wrong. I have even gotten to where I can predict this and have surprised many boy patients by correctly guessing the Barbie sticker they chose.

After years of playing this game, I have made an interesting observation. The trick works best on first-born children. In general, first-borns have more of a desire to please and are more likely to pick one of the first stickers I show them. Second-borns are more likely to want to see every sticker in the stack and are therefore, more difficult to predict.

A few years ago, my wife got me a Christmas present that has really added to the "end of visit sticker" game. She ordered a set of stickers of a picture of my face for me to give to my patients. I loved them!

Soon enough, I invented a new game to entertain my patients (and me). At the end of the visit, I will hold my sticker facing me and say, "I am going to show you a superhero. If you can tell me his name in two seconds, you can have two stickers from the stack."

I then turn my face sticker around usually to laughter as they scream, "That is not a superhero!"

Occasionally children do not recognize me, especially during the two Covid years when I was required to wear a mask. These children will blurt out Ironman (I don't really look like Tony Stark but I do have a goatee) or Spider-Man. I always tell them they are correct as the mom and I share a knowing look and give them two stickers.

This trick backfired somewhat when I decided to ask my patient, Jason, to name the superhero. Let me tell you a little bit about Jason. He was six years old—I know I should not say this about a child—but he was the meanest patient I have ever had. When he was younger, he was kicked out of numerous daycares and had already been suspended twice from kindergarten. I wasn't even aware that you could suspend a kindergartener. He was adopted as an infant and his parents were doing the best they could.

Every time I saw Jason, he would say something rude to me. I was not going to play the sticker game with him as I knew he would insult me. However, my curiosity got the best of me so I showed him my picture and asked, "Who is this superhero?"

He quickly answered, "Thor."

I said, "Thor. I like that!" and flexed my muscles.

Again, just as fast he responded, "No, I mean Thor in *Endgame* when he was really fat!"

How did he think of that so fast? I told you he was mean.

I like to pretend that I am a bit hurt when children do not ask for the stickers with my face on them. I do not have enough to give out, but always act like I have won a beauty contest when someone wants it.

This gave me an idea for a game to play with teen girls. At the end of the visit I say, "I am tired of your age group complaining about my sticker choices so I bought some Tom Holland and Harry Styles stickers."

They practically fall off the table saying they want one.

I then turn around the sticker with my large face smiling at them. They are always disappointed but have enough tact not to insult me like Jason did. When I started that game, I said I had Brad Pitt stickers but most of the teens had no idea who that was.

On another occasion, I had a grandmother of a teen embarrass me and her teen by saying, "I will take one of those Dr. Benfield stickers!"

The teen said, "Grandma!"

She replied, "Hey, he is cute!"

Take that Jason!

TORTURING THE STAFF

I HAVE SPENT THE LAST TWENTY-PLUS years working at the Shelby Children's Clinic and many of the staff have been with me the entire time. I know it is cliche to say it, but they are really like family to me.

During my time here, I have only had four nurses assigned to work with me. My first nurse, Amanda, was with me for ten years before she left to become a practice manager at another clinic. Then, I worked with Christy who went back to school and became an RN. My third nurse, Susie, was with me for eight years before she left to go work for the school system.

Currently, I am working with Kelsey who has been blessed with not one but two sets of twins! I imagine she will stick with me for a long time as having four small children at home will definitely give her a higher level of patience than the average person.

I find it amazing that I have not driven more nurses or staff away. I have never been mean or abrasive to them, however, my sense of humor can be a bit much to take at times. The following chapter is a behind-the-scenes look at my unique relationship with my staff.

When I arrived at the clinic for my first day, I was admittedly a bit nervous. I was met at the door by a nurse named Melissa. Her first words to me were, "I am going to be your nurse today. What would you like for lunch?"

I thought I had hit the jackpot. Someone was going to get me lunch every day! It turns out that we had a provider meeting that day and, in honor of my first day, the clinic was having lunch delivered. Sadly, I have rarely been asked that question again.

I then went upstairs where the physicians' offices were located and as I rounded a corner, I heard a nurse named Wanda say very loudly, "I need a man!"

I slowly backed up and said I must be in the wrong room. The nurse came after me with a very red face and explained she was lifting heavy boxes and meant she needed a man to help her. She then added she was happily married just to make sure I understood.

Like any other job, working as a physician can get repetitive at times. I have never been one to tolerate boredom so I often would entertain myself by playing jokes on the staff. April Fools' Day is obviously my favorite holiday. It meant I was basically granted free rein to prank the staff.

I started out harmlessly with the "quarter in the copier" trick. Basically, this involves making a few copies of a quarter, then putting the paper back into the printer.

Later, when my nurse made copies, it looked like there was a quarter stuck in the copier somewhere. I let her hunt for the coin for about five minutes before I told her what I had done.

Unfortunately, I forgot to remove the paper after showing her. I came out of a room from seeing a patient to find my nurse practitioner partner standing in front of a copier that had been totally disassembled. She had every drawer out and was looking quite irritated.

I sheepishly explained to her what I had done and as she walked away all I heard was, "Don't you have anything better to do with your time?" Evidently, I didn't.

Fast-forward to April 1, 2004. I had been at the clinic for five years and my staff was beginning to be on high alert whenever this day rolled around. I chose a nurse named Carol as my victim, in part, because she was good-natured but also a bit gullible.

We were still using paper charts back then and I left her a note saying the following, "Please call Mr. Lyon and ask him what he needs from me. He called earlier but did not leave a message."

She called the number I left for her and they answered, "North Carolina Zoo." I thought she would laugh and hang up but she had not gotten the joke.

She asked, "May I speak to Mr. Lyon?"

The lady on the other line laughed and said, "We have some lions here but none we call Mr. Lion."

Needless to say, Carol was not happy with me. I am sure she felt better when the staff got me back a few weeks later.

It was the end of the day on a Friday. I had taken my jacket off, thinking I was done for the day, when my nurse said, "You still have one more patient to see."

I trudged down the hall and the chart in the door had a chief complaint of "a little hoarse." I opened the door to find a small stuffed horse on the table. When I turned around, much of the staff, including Carol, were there to laugh at me.

April Fools' 2008 was my *coup de grace* (best prank ever). I had been planning this one for weeks and almost pulled the trigger the day before April 1 because I knew the staff would be expecting something.

Once the day arrived, I obtained a urine specimen cup from the lab, wrote a fake name on it, and filled it with warm Mello Yello. (Yes,

I warmed it, I told you I had thought this through). I then dropped a large chocolate-covered raisin in the cup and placed it in the small pass-through door between the restroom and the lab.

I loved that door. It had a waist-high shelf on the inside. Over the years, I had adorned it with a plastic rat, a fake cockroach, a live cricket, and a dollar bill with the words "urine doing a great job" written on it.

This time I knew Sandy, our lab tech and one of my good friends, would laugh at my joke and throw the cup in the trash. I was wrong. She thought it was real and was totally disgusted that some child had pooped in the cup.

My partner was in the lab at the time and described the scene to me. Sandy held her nose, hand-dipped the specimen with a urine dipstick, gagging twice, and then quickly put the specimen in the hazardous waste bin.

Five minutes later, there was a knock on my door. I opened it to find Sandy looking very upset. We went out into the hall and Sandy said, "Dr. Benfield, this child has diabetes!"

She then showed a printout with a 3+ sugar reading in the patient's urine. I looked back at her with a concerned look on my face and asked her what was the child's name?

She replied, "I.P. Freely."

It was amazing to watch her slowly rewind what had just happened as she began to comprehend that this was all a big joke. I watched her concerned face turn to anger as she turned and headed back to the lab. She refused to speak to me for three days.

I finally said, "Why are you so mad about this? I play jokes on you all the time."

She looked at me very seriously and said, "I was worried about that child!"

My reply insisting, "There was no child! It was Mello Yello!" did not help my case.

Fifteen years later, Sandy and I are still good friends, but the "Raisinette" incident is still not something I am allowed to bring up.

On the following April Fools' Day, I decided to tone things down a bit. I left a letter on the fax machine from a fake practice manager of a clinic in Kentucky saying he was excited that I was coming to work for them. It listed my starting date and a few random details.

It took all of fifteen minutes for that rumor to spread through the clinic. I noticed everyone would stop talking when I walked by and my nurse was not speaking to me.

Finally, my practice manager put an end to the charade when he noticed that the Kentucky "practice manager" in the letter shared a name with the current UNC Tar Heels' point guard and told everyone it was not real.

Many years later, a similar joke taught me an important lesson: do not mess with phone room staff. When the phone room folks come back at you, they go too far!

That year, my favorite holiday fell on my day off, but I was not to be deterred. I called in and, using a disguised voice, told the staff who answered that I was a realtor from Florida. I asked to speak to Dr. Cerjan (one of my partners) who was also off that day.

The staff member who answered asked if I wanted to leave him a message.

I explained that his offer on a house was accepted and that I looked forward to helping him relocate to Florida.

Again, wildfire doesn't spread this fast. Finally, one of the phone staff got up the nerve to call Dr. Cerjan. He convinced them he wasn't moving and reminded them what day it was. It didn't take the staff long to figure out the mastermind behind this prank.

I arrived at work the following day and I was disappointed that not much was said about my joke. Little did I know that the phone room staff was plotting their revenge behind the scenes.

I was seeing a patient right after lunch when there was a knock on my door. I opened it and was surprised to see a police officer standing there. He asked if we could speak somewhere private so we went into my office.

He brought out a small notebook that reminded me of Barney Fife's and read the following: "On March 25th, you backed into another vehicle in the parking lot of Walmart. You then left the scene of the accident without notifying anyone. Leaving the scene of an accident is a very serious crime."

He then folded his arms and stared at me aggressively. He had, however, made one mistake. I despise Walmart. I hate the effect it has had on small town America. It is also the number one spot where I am recognized by parents and hit up with medical questions. It had been more than a year since I had been to one.

As the silence between us grew uncomfortable, I reached into my pocket and pulled out my wallet and asked, "How much is it going to take to make this whole thing go away?"

He didn't blink! He just held his angry stare. They must teach this at the police academy. As I was beginning to think I had gone too far, he said, "At what point did you know this was a prank?"

I replied, "As soon as you said Walmart."

I asked if he could lead me out in handcuffs but he said that was going too far.

Oh, *that* would be too much? He had just come to my office and accused me of a made-up crime!

Luckily, the phone room staff was satisfied and didn't come after me again. I learned my lesson and never attempted to prank them again.

Of course, April 1st was not the only day I played jokes on the staff. However, the staff gave as good as they got. More than once I drove home with something tied to the back of my car or written on the side of it. I learned to hide my keys as oftentimes, at the end of the day, my car would be parked in a different area than I had left it that morning.

Our staff at the clinic has very little turnover and I think it is largely because it is such a fun place to work. I think the nurses like the fact that we don't have the typical doctor/nurse relationship. We are truly friends and they are free to pick on me just as often as I am on them.

Even when I am trying to be on my best behavior, situations will sometimes arise that have to be made fun of.

For example, one of my phone staff sent me a message saying the lab had called and a patient's blood culture was growing a bacteria resembling "staff."

I am sure that is what the lab said but what the nurse should have written was "staph" as in "staphylococcus" which is a type of bacteria.

For the next few days, I would bring other staff up to this nurse and ask, "Is this who the bacteria resembled?"

There were more times when I was presented with such a perfect opportunity, there was no way I could resist teasing my coworkers.

One of these occasions was when one of the front desk staff made the mistake of telling me about an embarrassing moment over the Christmas holidays. She had received a hot chocolate ball that was designed to be dropped into hot milk to make cocoa. However, she thought it was a bath bomb and dropped it into her bathtub!

She realized her mistake when she saw little marshmallows floating in the now-brown water. It took her hours to clean her tub—and months for me to stop reminding her about it.

It wasn't just the staff I tortured. My partners were fair game as well.

My last patient on a Friday afternoon left a very foul-smelling diaper in my examining room. I put the diaper in my partner Dr. Grinton's office and closed the door.

On Monday morning, I watched her walk into her office and I was giggling as I waited for her to scream. However, no noise came from her office. I felt like the Grinch when the Whos started singing. Where was the screaming? Why was she not running out of her office?

I went in to find her happily typing away in a normal-smelling office. The diaper was sitting on her bookcase where I had left it but it had no odor. I am still mystified today about this. Where did the smell go?

One of my other partners, Dr. Hendrix, has had the "privilege" of sitting beside me in the clinic for more than twenty years. She has tolerated bad jokes, pranks, and rude comments for all this time and never asked to move (to my knowledge).

Once, I got the clinic label maker (which I am now forbidden to use) and placed not-so-nice labels on her computer monitor. They are still there today, along with my face stickers that I placed all over the office with the caption "WWBD" (What Would Brian Do?).

Another of my favorite pastimes was to call the newborn nursery staff at the hospital using a disguised voice to ask all kinds of odd questions.

Sometimes, I would pretend to be a concerned mom with a teenage daughter who I thought was becoming sexually active. I would ask if my daughter could come look at all those babies so she would think twice before having sex.

Other times, I would pretend to be a local reporter from the newspaper and ask to interview the nurses about why our county had such a high fertility rate. I would tell them the title of the article was going to be: "Does Shelby Need a Bowling Alley?" (You know, to give people something ELSE to do.)

A dad called the nursery once with some odd questions and the nurse said, "We know this is you, Dr. Benfield. Good try."

The very confused dad said he would call back later. The nurse was embarrassed when she called the clinic and I confirmed it wasn't me!

Of course, my pranks didn't always go as planned as was the case when I called our local plastic surgeon's office. We had just lost one of our best receptionists to his office and I told my nurse we should call and beg her to come back. My nurse informed me that the surgeon was out of town and the employee was there by herself answering the phones.

So, I did what any professional person would do and called her up disguising my voice as a female. I explained that I was thinking of getting breast implants but I wanted to only have one side done first before committing to a pair. The nurse was very professional and told me she didn't think the doctor would do that.

I hung up and called her back five minutes later to tell her it was me and not a real caller. I was mortified to hear that during the meantime she had called the surgeon at the beach and ran the question by him! (His answer was no, by the way.) This surgeon was known to be very serious and I am sure he did not appreciate my attempt at humor.

Seven years later, I was meeting this doctor for the first time about having a cyst removed from my neck. He introduced himself and with a serious tone asked if I still wanted one breast implant.

I replied with a red face, "No, thank you. Just the cyst removal this time."

PHONE NOTES

Whenever I watch commercials on television the phrase "call your doctor" is used a lot. Like, "Before you start this workout, call your doctor," or "If you have an erection longer than four hours, call your doctor." I must admit, being "the doctor" that you are going to call gives me loads of anxiety. After hearing that phrase, I often think to myself, w*hat the heck am I going to do?* I wish the commercials would say "call your mom" or "call a really smart friend."

Some of the funniest moments at the clinic come via phone messages. Below is a list of some of the classics.

- "My four-year-old's nose smells funny!" After giving advice, mom hung up but called several minutes later to tell us she had found a large piece of sponge in his nose.
- "My one-month-old has a diaper rash and it is very itchy!" How does she know it is itchy? I have a mental image of the baby sticking one of those wooden scratchers down the back of its diaper.
- The mom of an eighteen-month-old with an irritated diaper area says she is "scooting across the floor on her bottom."
- A mom called at 1:30 a.m. because "my three-month-old is chewing on her hands."
- "My four-year-old has had a cough for one month and I can't take it anymore! Today is his birthday and he won't even eat his birthday cake!"

- "My three-year-old daughter smeared Chapstick all over her face and hair and I don't know what to do!"
- "My two-year-old swallowed twelve inches of dental floss!" I appreciated the exactness. Not eleven or thirteen inches of floss because that would have changed everything.
- "My two-year-old's stool looks like it has glitter in it." Truthfully, calls about stools are one of the most frequent calls we receive. Two of my favorites are the twenty-two-month-old having "clear stool" (I have no idea) and the preppy dad who described his three-year-old's stool as "hunter green." My least favorite description of stool and one we hear often is "like peanut butter." Sometimes I think about that when I am making a PB&J and gag a little.
- "My one-month-old is pulling at her ears."
- Once, on November 1, we received a call from a mom saying her nine-year-old son had abdominal pain and nausea. When prompted, she did remember that he ate lots of Halloween candy the night before.
- "My ten-year-old son jammed his finger playing video games."
- "I want my nine-month-old tested for ADHD."
- A mom called and reported her four-month-old was chewing on toys because his "gums itch really bad!"
- A dad called and said his seventeen-month-old daughter went into the corner after her bath and had a BM. She then proceeded to "take a large bite out of it!" He was calling to see if it was "toxic." Toxic—no. Disgusting—very much so!
- A three-year-old patient's mom called to tell me he had swallowed a penny. I told the mom that if he could eat bread without vomiting, he wouldn't have to come into the clinic. I also explained about

the "penny finding expedition" she would be going on in a day or so. She called back saying the child was refusing to eat the bread because he liked his doctor and wanted to see me.

As technology has evolved, parents are not only calling my office with questions, but they are also messaging me directly from their charts. Once, I had a mom overshare a bit using this technique. The message simply read, "The prunes worked!" When I clicked on the attachment, I was blessed with a close-up of an open diaper overflowing with stool.

HOLDING MY HEAD

When I sat down to write this book, my intention was to give a glimpse into how fun and joyful my life as a pediatrician has been. However, to give an accurate portrayal of my job, I must admit that it is not all jokes and laughter. There are situations that make me want to sit at my desk and hold my head. In this chapter, I will tell you about some of those instances.

The number one reason physicians choose to go into pediatrics is because we enjoy working with children. The reason many doctors are hesitant to choose this specialty is the misconception that most of the children's parents are going to be anxious or demanding.

On the contrary; most of the parents I work with are awesome and I consider many of them friends. However, there is a small subset who make me wish I had chosen to be a park ranger.

The first type of difficult parent I meet are the ones who arrive at the visit in an angry mood. Sometimes, they are angry because of something going on in their personal life or they just have a negative view of the world.

However, often it's the case that their child is not getting better and they are back for a second visit. Having a sick child is incredibly stressful and many parents tend to blame the pediatrician when an issue cannot be quickly solved.

I rarely see this when I take care of my own patients as there is a level of trust that has been fostered over the years. However, my clinic is large so I am often seeing patients who don't know me well. This is when I hear the phrase that all pediatricians dread: "Something has got to be done!"

Truthfully, when I first decided to write a book, I considered making this the title, but I knew only other pediatricians would understand the reference.

A typical use of this phrase goes something like this. "Little Jimmy has had diarrhea for a week, (pause for effect and then with extra volume) and SOMETHING HAS GOT TO BE DONE!"

This demand does nothing except add stress to the visit. Clearly, we are already doing the best we can and aren't withholding the "good" medicine until the parent gets angry.

When I am seeing an angry parent, I sit down with them and leave the computer off to make sure they feel heard. I make sure we agree on the plan for handling their child's illness and usually schedule a follow-up visit later in the week.

For most parents, this works to defuse the situation and they leave, if not happy, at least a little less angry.

However, there have been many times in my clinic when people leave so angry that our staff is concerned for their safety. I can think of half a dozen times when my partners have been afraid to walk to their cars because an angry parent is in the parking lot waiting for them.

Luckily, I have been spared this experience, but it is something all physicians have to worry about.

I did have a memorable angry mom call and give me an earful once. She had brought her child in to see me the day before and I had diagnosed him with a cold. I explained this was a virus and to take ibuprofen, drink plenty of liquids and the child would improve in a few days.

She called the next day and left a message with my nurse for me that said, "My child is still sick, his throat hurts, and you have got to do something. I am at Walmart waiting for you to call in some medicine to fix this."

I called her back and explained, "Ma'am, there are no antibiotics for this. This is a virus and it just has to run its course. If you would like, I would be happy to see him again to make sure nothing else is going on."

This made her furious and some not-so-nice words followed. She ended with, "That was your plan all along! You wanted us to come twice so you can get more of my money. Well, I am not paying another $10 copay to see you again!"

I apologized again and told her that was never my intent. More foul language was followed by, "Fine! I will just take him to the emergency room!"

Under normal circumstances, I suspect this mom does not behave like this. However, a sick child will turn many moms into "mama bears" and these times are very stressful for everyone involved.

Angry parents are not the only challenging parents I meet in my clinic. I often hear stories that are so odd, they make me, as I stated above, hold my head.

My first such parent was a lady who reported that her great grandson Lewis was having "death spells." She had become the primary caregiver for Lewis after both his mother and grandmother had been caught using drugs.

The first time I met Lewis he was six-months-old and was listed on my schedule as having death spells. According to his great grandmother, a spell is as follows: "He turns kind of pale and gets really cold and his heart rate goes down. He then looks dead."

If my life were a TV show, there would be a shot of me buzzing my nurse and telling her to cancel the rest of my afternoon appointments. However, in real life, that is impossible and I knew I would be late for the rest of my patients that day.

After taking a thorough history and not finding any abnormality on his exam, I called the pediatric hospital in Charlotte and had Lewis admitted. He stayed for two weeks and had nearly every test available. All his tests were normal and he went home on a heart monitor. Unfortunately, we were unable to make a diagnosis as he didn't have any of his spells while hospitalized.

I saw Lewis frequently over the next few years and could never find anything wrong with him. His great grandmother would report he was still having the spells about once per week but when the cardiologists would analyze the monitor, there was never any evidence that anything had occurred.

The last time I saw him before his mom regained custody of him, I asked his great grandmother if his monitor had gone off lately.

She replied, "No. I don't use it anymore. It was not any good. When he has a spell, I revive him myself."

Alarmed, I asked her how she "revives" him?

"I just lightly tap on his chest with my finger and he comes back. Although sometimes he self-resuscitates himself."

That brought up a mental image of a small, nine-month-old infant giving himself chest compressions, but I quickly shook that off and reminded myself that I am a professional and not ten years old.

Shortly after this visit, Lewis' mom got off drugs and resumed custody of him. He never had another "death spell" and I (and you) will never know what, if anything, was going on with him.

One of the most difficult situations to deal with in my job is called Munchausen syndrome. Classically, people with this disorder fake illness to draw attention or sympathy to themselves. When a parent does this with a child it is called Munchausen by proxy. This is difficult to diagnose as many of the parents have researched diseases on the internet and know just how to describe their child's symptoms.

I have been quite surprised at the number of these cases that I have seen over the years. Most of the parents only stayed with me for a few years, because as soon as I started becoming suspicious, they would switch to another clinic.

The other thing that occurs is the children become old enough to speak for themselves and deny what their parents are reporting.

A typical parent does not want their children to be hospitalized or to undergo laboratory testing, so why do these parents do this? The most common reason is attention. Many of these cases involve moms who are in a relationship where no one pays much attention to them. As soon as they show up at a doctor's office describing something serious going on with their child, they have an instant audience. People at church and on social media reach out to them to wish them well and to pray for them. This only feeds their desire to make up new stories.

I have too many of these stories to relay here but I will tell you about a few of my most interesting. The first mom came in to see me with her six-week-old baby with the chief complaint of "worm in stool."

I had already suspected this mom of Munchausen by proxy with her first baby. With that child, she had reported such bad reflux and vomiting that I hospitalized the child for three days. Sure enough, he never spit up or vomited while there.

When I entered the room, she immediately handed me a diaper and said, "Look what was in his poop."

I opened the diaper to find a small amount of stool and a small white worm. She had picked the wrong doctor to try to fool because I grew up in the country. I quickly recognized this to be a small "grub" worm like you would find under a log in the woods. (Do not look up an image of this online. They are disgusting.)

Besides that, the worm was fully intact and obviously had not passed through someone's GI tract. Not to mention the fact that newborns rarely have worms because they are not old enough to play in the dirt and ingest the larvae like older kids do.

I put on my psychologist hat and calmly told mom that this worm had to be put in the diaper by someone and gently asked if she wanted to talk about any issues she was having at home. She became angry and left the office and that was the last time I saw her (or the worm).

The next Munchausen by proxy case involved a three-month-old baby who came in on a Thursday morning because she had blood in her stool. The mom brought the baby in without an appointment and demanded to be seen. My nurse assured her that we could work the baby in to be seen in an hour or so, but the mom demanded to be seen right then or she was taking the baby to the hospital.

A baby with blood in the stool is a serious problem, so I immediately had the nurse put them in a room and I came in right after. The mom was rocking back and forth in her chair, very agitated. She said, "Please help my baby. She has been pooping blood all night long!"

I immediately went over to look at the baby and she was smiling up at me and laughing. Her color was good and her heart rate was normal so I was at least partially reassured.

I asked the mom if she had brought any of the diapers with blood in them and she handed me one sealed in a plastic bag. (As you can see from my stories, I get handed a lot of diapers to examine.)

What I found in the diaper was some loose stool and a large amount of bright red liquid which had stained the diaper.

"This does not look like blood," I told the mom.

"It is definitely blood." replied the mom.

"Well, there is one way to find out. I can do a test called a Hemoccult, which will tell us if there is any blood in the stool."

Now mom was getting concerned and added, "Is that accurate? Don't you think she should be hospitalized?"

I told her I did not think that would be necessary and was surprised she wasn't happy to hear that her baby was likely not sick. I then took the stool to my lab tech, Sandy, who took one look at the diaper and said, "That's not blood!"

We then performed the test on the red areas in the diaper and, sure enough, the Hemoccult test was negative for blood. Sandy then smelled the diaper and reported, "I know this smell. This is cherry Kool-Aid!"

When I gently told the baby's mom of our findings, as expected, she became angry and left. I was a bit more concerned for this baby's well-being given the mom's mental status. I reported the case to social services. Unfortunately, they could not find enough during their investigation to intervene and the mom never returned to our clinic.

As I mentioned, some moms with Munchausen by proxy are so good at feigning symptoms that it is almost impossible to prove what they are doing. One notable situation like this involved a two-year-old male named Simon. I first met him when he was ten months old and had come in for vomiting.

When I asked the mom how long the vomiting had been going on she answered, "Since birth!"

She then went on to tell me that he had been hospitalized three times for this at three different hospitals and that no one could figure out what was wrong with him.

I remember being reassured that he was growing well, but still very concerned about why he was so sick. Most people I meet are honest, so at this point the idea that his mom was making up his symptoms was the furthest thing from my mind. Given all this, I referred him to a pediatric gastroenterologist.

Now, Simon was two and had been seen by the specialist four times with no definitive diagnosis found for his vomiting. He even underwent upper and lower endoscopy under anesthesia with normal findings.

After the endoscopy, the GI specialist called me and said, “Simon’s mom reports he is vomiting two to three times each day. However, his esophagus looked totally normal. If he was truly vomiting that much, I should have been able to see damage to his esophagus.”

So, we devised a plan. We told mom we were going to try a new medicine that had to be given in the hospital and that we would need to keep Simon in the hospital for a few days. We then put him in a room with a camera built into the ceiling looking at the crib. This room was used for seizure patients so that any subtle seizure activity could be recorded and looked at later.

The next week, I received a call from the GI specialist. He reported, “We have figured out what is wrong with Simon and it only took a few hours. Right after lunch, his mom put him in his crib. After he fell asleep, she took the leftover food on his lunch tray and spread it out over his chest and crib. She then added a bit of milk on the railing and mattress for effect.”

Case closed! We called social services and the child was removed from the home until the mom could get the psychological help she needed.

An issue that makes all physicians hold their heads is drug-seeking patients. In general, pediatricians are less affected by this than doctors who care for adults but we are by no means exempt.

During my first few years working in the clinic, I was bombarded by calls for cough medicine with codeine. These parents had a habit of calling at 4:45 in the afternoon to report their child was coughing horribly. Invariably, they would ask for the "strongest cough medicine" we had.

They knew it was too late for their child to come in and if my nurse offered them an appointment for the next day, they would say, "But my child hasn't slept in two nights. I don't know if we can make it through another one."

Thankfully, about fifteen years ago, the FDA banned these medicines in children and the calls have decreased. We still have to deal with the parents wanting pain medicine, however. Shelby does not have many pediatric dentists so we frequently get calls from parents whose children have dental pain and can't be seen by a dentist for a couple of weeks.

Most of these are legit and, thankfully, can be managed with antibiotics and ibuprofen. But some are obviously drug-seeking parents. Offering the patient an appointment is usually the easiest way to discern between the two as the drug seekers obviously do not have a bad tooth to show us.

I had one mom who called frequently asking for narcotics for her children's teeth. She became tired of me saying no and decided to take it to another level. She first called on a Tuesday with the complaint that she needed pain medicine for her sixteen-year-old child's abscessed tooth. I told her I would be happy to see him and when she declined, I told her to try ibuprofen.

She called back on Wednesday and sent the same message to my partner who forwarded the message to me. When I again gave her the same options she told my nurse, "I need you to call in something stronger than ibuprofen. The tooth is so bad I can see the nerve sticking through it!"

I decided to call that bluff and called mom back personally. I told her I had a friend who is a dentist and he could work her child in today. She responded by saying, "Just forget it!" and slammed the phone down.

During my training as a pediatrician, the most pervasive message was DO NOT OVERUSE ANTIBIOTICS. It was common during rounds for an attending physician to be describing the events leading up to a child being hospitalized by saying, "He was given antibiotics by his local pediatrician for 'itis.'" As this was said, the attending doctor would make air quotes with his fingers. This would be followed by quiet murmuring by everyone in attendance.

Giving antibiotics for a viral infection not only leads to bacteria becoming resistant, it can also be dangerous. For example, a patient with meningitis or appendicitis will appear better for a few days when taking oral antibiotics. However, this delays their diagnosis which can be catastrophic.

Therefore, when I arrived in Shelby to start practicing, I was determined to only use antibiotics when absolutely necessary. Unfortunately, I was not expecting the culture that exists in most rural areas regarding viral infections. More than half of the parents I encountered did not want to hear that their child had a virus. They wanted antibiotics and they wanted them right then.

Most of these parents had been trained by their parents and grandparents that any fever or cough needs antibiotics. This was made worse by the fact that some of the senior partners in the group had not done much to combat this.

Below are the most common responses from a parent upon hearing that their child did not need antibiotics:

"I waited an hour in the waiting room and you are not giving me any medicine?"

"Fine, I will just go to the emergency room."

"Do you not see how green his mucus is?"

"But we have a birthday party this weekend!"

"He never gets any better unless he takes antibiotics. And do not give him amoxicillin. That does not work for my child."

How big a problem is this? I will answer this by admitting that I am pressured to give unnecessary antibiotics almost every day and this is incredibly tiring.

Luckily, there were other young pediatricians hired around the same time I was. Together, we have worked hard at educating the community on this subject. I am pleased to say that the majority of parents who choose me as their children's primary doctor either agree with my stance on antibiotics or at least tolerate it.

The next situation that makes being a pediatrician difficult is when the parents of my patient are divorced. Of course, this is not always the case as many parents continue to co-parent beautifully even when living in separate homes.

The most difficult times are when I see a child with both divorced parents present.

Often the interaction will go something like this: "So, is little Johnny drinking his milk?

Mom: "At my house he does."

Dad: "He drinks tons at my house."

Mom: "That is not true. Johnny says you never have any milk in the house!"

Dad: "I always have milk! Doctor, will you tell her he doesn't need to go to bed by ten on weekends."

Mom: "Tell him he needs his sleep! Otherwise, he has trouble getting up on Monday mornings at my house."

These visits are never fun and sometimes I don't even wait until I get to my desk to start holding my head.

Even when only one parent comes to the visit, the divorce can be a big part of the visit.

It is common for me to hear phrases like, "She is always sick when he comes back from her mom's house" or "His grades are slipping because his dad doesn't make him do his homework."

The most common complaint I hear from moms is, "He comes back from his dad's house behaving horribly. His dad lets him do whatever he wants and there are no rules."

I tell all my parents when they are separating that the most important thing for a child is stability. Both homes need to have similar rules about behavior, eating, and bedtimes.

Of course, children love going to the "party house" with dad where they get to stay up late and eat what they want, but studies have shown that what children really need is continuity. Having similar rules and parenting styles in both homes is comforting and helps children grow up without any psychological baggage from the divorce. For two people who no longer want to live together this is a difficult thing to manage.

I once had a mom come in with her six-year-old son complaining that her child wanted to live with his dad because he had a better time there on the weekends than with her during the week.

I told her this was common and mentioned how dads are sometimes not as comfortable in their role as authoritarian and end up trying to become more of a friend than a parent.

She said, "You have no idea. His dad owns a professional auto racing team. Every weekend they fly to a racetrack and my son hangs out with famous people and race car drivers!"

I did not have a good reply for that one.

The biggest complaint most people have about going to see a doctor is the time spent waiting. I think this is a good place to discuss the many reasons why there is a wait.

At least in pediatrics, one big reason we fall behind is the huge volume of children we are asked to see each day. Because of this volume, our clinic overbooks our schedules on most days. I would love to see fewer patients and have time for coffee and scones (I really do not like either of these two things), but in my clinic we strive to see children the same day the parents call us.

There are many reasons to see a pediatric patient quickly. First, children can become severely ill much more rapidly than adults. Secondly, many parents have to miss work when their child is sick and they want to be seen by a doctor as soon as possible. Thirdly, we love our children and do not want them to suffer any longer than necessary.

Another reason there could be a long wait to see a physician is the fact that some illnesses take longer to treat than the time allotted. For example, the child scheduled for a short visit for a fever may actually be very ill or have a complex medical history and require labs or more time overall.

There are a few more reasons a pediatrician will fall behind: (a) patients who arrive late (do not get me started); (b) the unexpected sick sibling; and (c) the "Oh, by the way …" moments.

Any parent with more than one child knows that if one of their kids gets sick, the other is soon to follow. Going to the doctor is expensive so, when this happens, many parents bring both children in for one appointment hoping to get a two-for-one special. I have three children and so I understand this mentality. However, as a pediatrician, it can really wreck your day. The schedule is already tight and so seeing the sibling adds fifteen minutes that I don't have.

When a parent says, "I brought his or her sibling along, hoping you can check them, too," it puts me in an unwinnable situation. If I see the sibling, I am now going to be even later than usual for the rest of my patients that shift. This makes the parents of those future patients unhappy and left wondering why am I taking so long.

It may sound like the obvious answer is to not see the extra sibling. However, it is almost impossible for me to look at a coughing or feverish child and tell them I cannot see them. It feels mean and uncaring and that is not who I am. Moreover, sometimes the parent called and asked for both children to be seen but there was only one appointment slot left. If you were that parent, would you like to have to choose which one of your children is the sickest?

There are no easy answers. I simply check the extra children and spend the remainder of the shift apologizing to the rest of my patients. And then you'll find me sitting at my desk and holding my head at the end of the day.

As for the "Oh, by the way …" moments, this is the phrase that pediatricians have nightmares about.

Why are these words so terrifying? Because this is almost always followed by one or more complex questions that are impossible to answer in a timely manner and have nothing to do with why the appointment was made.

There are other variants on this phrase such as, "Uh, while I am here …" or "Hey, just one more thing …."

All of which have the potential to add large amounts of time to a schedule that is already too constricting.

Here are some common examples of what follows this innocent "ask" of me:

"He has been having abdominal pain (or headaches) lately."

"Can you tell me how to potty train my child?"

"I don't know how to handle her behavior."

"I think he may have autism."

"The teacher says she may have ADHD."

"My baby breathes funny sometimes."

I am not exaggerating when I say these are almost daily occurrences in pediatrics. I have tried responding with, "This is a complex issue and, unfortunately, we are out of time today. Could I see you for this on another day?"

That sounds fine in writing, but when I say it, the parents hate it because they have already taken time off work for this appointment.

I usually try to slow down and answer their questions in as complete a manner as I can and offer them a return visit if they would like to discuss it further.

It is not uncommon when I ask one of my partners how their day went to hear, "It was going well but then I had two "Oh, by the ways …" and got way behind."

So, if your doctor is late for your visit, chances are they had an "Oh, by the way …" or two before it was time to see you.

I was discussing how much I hated getting behind with a patient once and they asked, "What do you care if you are running late? I am the one who had to wait."

The truth is, getting behind can affect the quality of the work that I do. For example, when my nurse tells me I have six people waiting on me, I feel rushed and stressed. Neither of which are emotions that I want my doctor to feel when he walks into my room. I like to spend a lot of time with each of my patients and being behind certainly affects that.

Even though my job can sometimes make me sit at my desk and "hold my head," I have very little room to complain. Compared with the difficulties most people face in their jobs, mine are inconsequential. So, thank you for allowing me a chapter to vent!

Being a pediatrician has been a fabulous career choice for me and I cannot picture myself doing anything else. I hope this chapter has given you a window into what this job is like daily. It is not all laughter and fun, but even when I have a day filled with issues like those mentioned above, I know that my next room likely contains a small child who will do their best to make it all better by making me laugh or smile. What other occupation has that?

LAUGHTER AT MY HOUSE

Let's face it, all parents think their own kids are the funniest in the world and I am no different. If you are one of those people who hate to listen to people talk about their children, feel free to skip this chapter. Really, it is okay. There is no big exam at the end of the book.

One of the things people don't realize is that physicians often are older before we start having children because our training is so long. Ellen and I had our first child, Griffin, when I was in my last year of training and twenty-eight years old. Being older did not make me wiser and I learned more about being a parent from taking care of Griffin than all of my pediatric training.

Luckily, even though he was the first—and in many ways—the practice child, he managed to grow into a successful adult. He graduated from the University of North Carolina at Charlotte in three years and he now is a police officer in a nearby city.

One of the most useful things Griffin taught me was that potty training can be incredibly difficult. During my training, I heard lots of tips on this subject and when Griffin was two, I even read a book about it. Griffin quickly showed me that no amount of knowledge was a match for a toddler who did not want to sit on the toilet. My wife and I tried every trick known to man and he would not budge.

I received an early warning that he was not going to be easy to train when was two. I was changing his diaper and he announced, "When I get big, I am going to change my own diaper!"

As he was closing in on three, I admit it was a bit embarrassing for the pediatrician's child to be the only one in his preschool class to not be using the potty. We finally started making some progress using the sticker chart until he figured out a way to work that system.

I came home at lunch and he met me at the door with his chart and said, "Look Daddy! I got eight stickers today!"

I remember thinking Ellen must have needed to up the reward to get him to go, but I was happy for any progress.

This feeling quickly evaporated when my tired-looking wife came in and explained, "He keeps pooping tiny amounts in order to get a sticker and then asking to go again ten minutes later." Finally, a few months after his third birthday, he finally "agreed" to use the potty full time.

When I discuss potty training with the parents in my clinic, I explain to them that the term "potty training" is incorrect. We are not training our children to use the toilet, instead we are tasked to find ways to make our children want to do it. This process can be more complex than any big business negotiation and depends more upon the personality of the child than the knowledge of the parent.

One of the things that all new parents have to learn on their own is that hosting a birthday party with a bunch of small children is never as fun as you think it will be. After having two such parties at our house, I had the bright idea to have Griffin's seventh birthday party at a local arcade called Bubba's Fun Park.

Things were going great until one of the children named Wesley came up to me in tears. I quickly noticed that his blue jeans were soaked and based on the odor I knew this was not water.

I channeled my inner Andy Griffith and took Wesley to the bathroom where I used the automatic hand dryer and dried his pants to the point that the stain was less visible. I then gave him a bunch of game tokens and he went happily back into the arcade.

I was explaining to Ellen how my quick thinking had saved the day when I heard someone say, "Hey, Dr. Benfield. Look at me!"

I turned to see Wesley laying in the ball pit in his urine-soaked jeans!

Feeling less proud of myself, I "fished" Wesley out of the ball pit and we headed home early.

One of the things I was not prepared for as a parent was how to handle it when Griffin became old enough to notice girls. When he was only eight years old, he made a comment that made me think I was going to have to have the "talk" well before I was expecting to.

Let me preface this story by explaining that Griffin had always used the word "pickles" when describing someone's chest. This started when he was very young and threw a ball and hit me in the chest causing me to say, "Ow! You hit me in the nipple!"

He thought I said "pickle" and from that day on that was the word he used to mean someone's chest.

Fast-forward to when he was eight and we were leaving our local YMCA after a basketball game. As we walked out, there was a small festival in the parking lot. At the first table we came to, there was a lady selling sandwiches. The lady in question was wearing a tight tank top and as we were walking by, Griffin nudged my arm and nodded toward her.

I was shocked when he said, "Look at those huge pickles!"

My first instinct was to smack him in the back of the head and tell him how inappropriate that was. As I turned to do this, I caught a glimpse of something on the table. It was a large glass jar full of … giant pickles!

I then replied to Griffin, "Yes, those are huge pickles."

Thankfully, I had a few more years before we had to have the "talk."

Two years after Griffin was born, Ellen and I had a daughter and named her Keeley. I was aware that second-borns can be a handful from listening to other parents' difficulties, including my mom since I am a second-born myself. However, we had already done this once and so we felt very confident we could handle the next child as well. What no one tells you is that each child is different, therefore, you need to parent each child differently. Consequently, you never really get "great" at parenting and are always having to adapt your style to the child you are dealing with at that moment.

I try to pass this bit of advice on to all the parents in my clinic and remind them that parenting books are only meant as guidelines. You must adapt these guidelines to fit your child.

I think people have the misconception that pediatricians are great at parenting because of all our training. My training taught me how to take care of a child with pneumonia but when faced with a screaming toddler in a restaurant, I am just as stressed and bewildered as any other parent.

I feel that is why God sent me Keeley. She taught me more about how to parent a strong-willed child than any book or behavioral specialist. Now, whenever a parent is having a hard time with their child, I can tell them I have been through similar experiences and explain what worked or didn't work for me.

I can also reassure them that even though Keeley was difficult, she has grown into a wonderful compassionate adult who just graduated from the University of North Carolina at Chapel Hill (my alma mater!) and has a bright future ahead of her.

I could devote an entire chapter to "butting heads with Keeley" but I will just give you a few highlights. When the kids were small, I was in charge of bath time. Usually, this was a fun bonding time. However, on one memorable occasion when Griffin was four and Keeley was two, things went south quickly.

They had not been in the tub long when Keeley started splashing Griffin.

I gave her my best stern look and said, "If you do that one more time, you are going to have to get out."

Predictably, she looked me right in the eye and splashed Griffin in the face.

One of the most important rules of parenting is "Do not make empty threats." So, I picked her up and set her on the floor beside me as I got up to get a towel.

That's when I simultaneously heard Griffin gasp and the sound of a liquid hitting the floor. I turned to see Keeley standing with her legs spread and peeing on the floor as she looked at me angrily.

I quickly started heading toward her saying, "Oh, no you don't!"

She turned to run and immediately slipped and landed right on her back in a big puddle of urine!

For a moment I forgot I was a parent and thought I was watching *America's Funniest Home Videos*. I pointed at her and let out a huge laugh.

This did not make her happy and she started crying loud enough that I am sure our neighbors heard.

This shocked me back into parent mode. I took her hand and was trying to help her up when I heard Griffin—who had been hysterically laughing—suddenly made a gurgling noise. He was laughing so hard he had slipped under the water!

So, please make a mental picture of me holding two children up in the air by their arms. One child is screaming and covered in urine and the other is coughing up bath water. All the while I am simultaneously screaming for my wife. I still have PTSD from this bath time experience.

Shortly after this adventure, we were sitting at the dinner table when I glanced out at the sandbox I had proudly built for the kids. I had put a lot of work into this project and it bothered me that the kids rarely played in it.

I told a small fib by saying, "Tomorrow there's a guy who is coming to take our sandbox home to his children. You guys don't play in it and he says his kids would love it."

Griffin immediately dropped his fork, ran outside, and got into the sandbox, and waved at us through the window.

I turned to two-year-old Keeley and said, "Well?"

She responded with, "You are not the boss of me, Brian!"

Nowhere in the "Parenting Handbook" does it tell you how to handle this.

Karma finds a way to pay back everyone, even adorable children. When Keeley was in kindergarten she came home and told us that the corn Ellen had packed her for lunch had tasted funny. Ellen did not remember sending corn so Keeley handed her the "sour cream" container that we often filled with fruit and veggies in the children's lunch boxes. When we opened it up there was a little bit of corn left as well as some pieces of grass.

My brain quickly flashed back to the day before when Griffin and I had used that corn for bait as we fished at a local lake. We had handled many fish, hence giving the corn that "funny" flavor.

Ellen had accidentally sent that container to school instead of the identical one which was filled with fruit.

I was even more embarrassed when I heard that Keeley's teacher had microwaved it for her and had asked about the bits of grass sprinkled throughout.

When we explained to Keeley what happened she exclaimed, "Fish corn! I am going to call a DDS!"

I did not tell her that the correct abbreviation for the Department of Social Services is DSS and I didn't mind if she called a DDS (i.e., a dentist).

Because Keeley was so headstrong, Ellen and I waited four years before we decided we wanted to have another child. Our third and final daughter is Meredith. She is currently a first-year student at the University of North Carolina at Chapel Hill and interested in working in the medical field.

This was not what I thought she would do when she was little as she was always a bit squeamish when it came to blood and bodily fluids. When she was four, she was sitting beside me one day when I received a call from a mom whose child had a stomach virus. I told the mom I would send the child in some suppositories to help with the vomiting.

Meredith asked, "What are suppositories?"

I explained them to her and she started gagging and said that was the most disgusting thing she had ever heard.

I replied, "It's no big deal. We have some in our refrigerator."

She screamed, "Next to our food?"

She did not feel any better when I added, "They are not bottom-flavored before you use them."

Meredith has inherited my love of horses and has been fortunate enough to grow up on a farm with a barn and a couple of horses. We live far enough out in the country that we often have coyotes around our property and this made the horses very anxious. They were constantly staring into the woods and seemed on edge. I had heard that donkeys would protect horses and so answered an ad from a farmer selling mini donkeys. The man assured me that even a mini donkey would protect a horse.

So, I loaded up the kids and we drove one hour to the farm to pick out a donkey. As soon as we walked into the pasture, a young, black mini donkey came over to us and allowed the kids to pet her. The farmer said that she was a female and that the females cost twice as much as males.

"Get away from that one," I told the kids. "Let's go look at the males."

Unfortunately for me, the males were wild and would not let us near them. We still managed to pick one out and the farmer said he would deliver him in a couple of weeks.

The entire way home, all the kids could talk about was how much they loved the little black female donkey.

Predictably, I called the farmer the next day and told him we wanted the little female.

He said, "She is so small that if you have a large dog crate you could pick her up yourself and not wait the two weeks."

Because I was running for Father of the Year, I surprised Meredith by getting her out of elementary school early the next day and we drove to the farm.

When we arrived, I said, "You pick out whichever donkey you want."

She was so excited and ran to the small female and said, "I want this one. Can we really have her?"

I was having one of those days that fathers dream about until I unloaded the foldable wire dog crate.

The farmer took one look at it and said, "I said a big dog crate. She won't fit in that."

Meredith overheard and said sadly, "So, we can't take her home with us?"

The farmer replied, "She would fit in the back of your SUV."

I laughed at what I thought was a joke. My SUV was only two years old and there was no way I was putting a donkey in the back of it. But then I turned and looked at Meredith's sad face. Five minutes later, we are putting shavings in the back.

Meredith got into the back seat and the farmer lifted the donkey into the back as I quickly slammed the hatch. I knew she would not be happy back there but I had not anticipated that she would try to jump into the back seat until Meredith started screaming. I got into the back with Meredith and we used the wire cage to block half of the opening. I then found an umbrella and opened it to block the rest of the space.

We started driving the one-hour trip home with me looking in the rearview mirror and constantly moving the umbrella back and forth to block her from jumping over the seat.

About five minutes into the trip Meredith screamed, "She's pooping!"

I replied under my breath with some non-child-friendly words.

Fifteen minutes into the trip Meredith announced, "She's peeing!"

I had no idea a donkey could pee this much as it seemed to last for five minutes. That was nothing because when we were almost home, she beat that record by peeing for what seemed like eight minutes.

Things got worse when we were at a stoplight and I noticed people in other cars staring and pointing at us. I told Meredith to look straight ahead and not to make eye contact with anyone. I prayed no one would recognize us. I did not want to end up being a story on Facebook.

We finally got her home and when I opened the hatch she jumped out of the back like a rocket.

Thankfully, "Jenny" has been a wonderful addition to the family. The horses were much calmer with their little protector and we enjoyed letting her out of the fence to hang around the yard with us. We even had a pool party once with her walking around the pool trying to eat people's food and occasionally nipping someone's bum (never turn your back on a mischievous donkey). How many people can say they have been to a pool party with a mini donkey present?

As for my SUV, it never fully recovered. Many cleanings and air fresheners could not totally cover up the smell. Or maybe it was all in my head (more mental trauma).

Over the years, I have had parents thank me for my advice and tell me that I must be a great father. In truth, parenting is hard for all of us. Even though I sound smart in my white coat, my children made sure I never felt too confident. They were also quick to remind me of my "true status" in our family.

On one occasion when Griffin was five, he said, "Thanks for supper, Mom. You can really cook!" He then turned to me and added. "And you are a good cereal cooker, Dad!"

Perhaps worse was when Meredith was three and we were watching *Mary Poppins*. The father in the family was yelling at the children. Meredith asked, "Why is he yelling like that?"

I answered with the first thing that came to mind which was, "I guess he's trying to show that he is in charge."

Meredith thought about this for a few seconds and then announced, "Mom is in charge of our family."

She was not wrong, but I guess I gave her a disappointed look so she quickly added, "But you are like the … babysitter when she is not home."

I didn't tell her that even that wasn't true as her older sister seemed to be filling that role recently.

Boy, am I glad the parents in my clinic did not hear that one.

I am not the only one who has kept notes on funny things in my life. Ellen also wrote journals of the clever, memorable, and silly things our children said and did. I highly recommend writing down these moments to any new parent. For me, it has been a joy to take a trip down memory lane. My kids have especially enjoyed reading all the hilarious things they did, too.

Unfortunately, I decided to read these journals so I could write this chapter the same week as I am dropping my youngest child at college. So, even though I laughed a lot, many tears were also shed as I reminisced about my time with these small comedians. As you enjoy these last few quotes from my children, remember to hold your own kids close and enjoy every minute (even when your three-year-old is still wearing a diaper!).

When Meredith was eighteen-months-old, I saddled up my horse and put her on his back for the first time. She kicked her tiny legs but the horse obediently stood still so she turned to me and said, "Push me!"

I called home from work one day and my wife put two-year-old Keeley on and told her someone wanted to talk to her.

"Hi Keeley."

"What you name?"

"Keeley. It's Daddy."

"He say him name Daddy!"

Ellen told five-year-old Meredith we were going to go see a friend of ours. She replied, "Is that the one from Nappingville?"

Ellen was a bit confused and explained that she was from Waco.

"I knew it had something to do with sleeping."

I was watching a UNC basketball game on television and said, "Time out! Roy, you need a time-out!"

Three-year-old Griffin got up from playing and looked at me very concerned, "He needs a time-out?"

Ellen and Meredith were picking up shells on the beach when a woman walked past them. Meredith, who was three at the time, shouted, "Stop walking on our shells!"

At age four, Griffin announced to everyone that he had to "poop" and headed for the bathroom. He came out shortly after and let us know that "his bottom had changed its mind."

Meredith and I were catching lightning bugs when she was two and she asked, "Why do they light up like that?"

"That is how they talk to each other."

"They talk with their bottoms!"

When Keeley was three, she begged us to get a cat. Every time we gave a reason why that was a bad idea, she came up with a solution. Once, mainly to amuse Ellen, I said, "We can't get a cat, they spend too much of their day licking the butter."

I received the desired look from Ellen that said "funny but inappropriate." Keeley, however, took it to heart and told her preschool teacher about it adding, "I don't understand why we can't just put up the butter."

I was in the bathroom helping the plumber work on our sink when Meredith came home from preschool and announced very loudly, "What is that man smell? Is there a man here, cause I smell man smell?"

WHO AM I?

Now that you have read how hilarious and eventful the life of a pediatrician can be, I want to tell you a little about myself and how I came to write this book. If you have no interest in this very important subject, you may close the book and our time together is over. Really, it's okay. I will never know.

I grew up in Lenoir, North Carolina, another small town about one hour north of my current home in Shelby. I had a knack for humor, even as a small child, leading to my antics being published in the *Charlotte Observer* newspaper column written by Kays Gary. Mr. Gary wrote a public interest column and would occasionally include funny stories sent in from his readers.

My first inclusion came when I was in kindergarten and had a role in the annual Christmas play. I was the narrator and announced the following line to the entire audience, "Mary and Joseph were heading to Bethlehem because Mary 'HEARD' she was going to have a baby."

After this appeared in the paper, my grandmother asked me if any of my friends had commented on it to me.

I replied, "My friends don't read the *Charlotte Observer*!"

Which led to my second appearance in the column, with Kays adding, "If I don't watch out, this kid is going to have my job!"

Interestingly, Mr. Gary, who was incredibly popular during his twenty-five years writing for the *Observer*, grew up just north of Shelby and is buried eight miles from my home.

Being written about in the paper was a cool honor for a kid, however, it was more common for my quick wit to lead to a visit to the principal or, at the very least, to cause my teachers to give me a disapproving look over their glasses. My first-grade teacher made me spend the entire year in a seat right beside her desk so she could keep my antics to a minimum.

When I was young, I had no intention of being a doctor. Instead, I had my heart set on becoming a veterinarian. I loved animals and we always had plenty of dogs and cats around the house. When I was in sixth grade, I went to a summer camp and rode my first horse. I was instantly hooked and came home begging for one of my own.

My parents bought me "Scout" who was very patient as I literally learned how to ride on him. I spent the next few years riding Scout on all the back roads near my home. I can honestly say these were among the happiest times of my life. I mowed yards to make money for Scout's feed and hay and rode my bike one mile to his barn before and after school every day to feed him.

In eighth grade, I was doing very poorly in school. My mom promised me any pet I wanted if I would bring my grades up. She was sure I would choose a puppy but we already had a dog. I had bigger plans for this unrestricted offer. Unfortunately for her, I had just watched the movie *The Beastmaster*, a film featuring two ferrets. After making straight As, we went to the pet store and much to my mother's chagrin, left with a ferret of my own. I could then be found on weekends riding Scout with my ferret in my saddlebag just like the character in the movie.

I sold Scout at age eighteen before I left for college. All these years later, I still get a pit in my stomach when I think about how hard that was. How do you get over selling your best friend? I have had many horses as an adult, but I have never been able to replicate the bond I had with Scout.

Growing up with all these animals was not the only reason I wanted to be a veterinarian. The other reason was that I looked up to our local vet, Dr. John Thuss. He was a friend of the family and often made house calls for our animals. As I watched him give our dogs vaccines while simultaneously having conversations with my mother, I knew that was the job for me.

As I grew older, Dr. Thuss inadvertently influenced my decision to go to medical school instead of vet school. What I am about to admit is embarrassing but, before you judge me, remember I was only sixteen years old at the time.

At this age, I started noticing that Dr. Thuss always drove an old beaten-up Subaru which was rusting so bad that you could almost see through the doors. I decided that if this is what a vet drove, then maybe I should be a medical doctor.

Shallow? Definitely. It only gets worse. Dr. Thuss told me years later that he had a nice car, and that the Subaru was just his work car! If he had a nicer work car who knows how my life would have turned out! Animals are not nearly as funny as children so I likely would never have written a book!

Even though I was a good student, going to school was like torture to me. Like many of my patients, being cooped up in a building all day felt like punishment. Knowing this about me, my parents were concerned I would not follow through on my plans for higher education. Therefore, they had the bright idea to show me what the real world was like.

My summer before college, my dad talked me into working at the furniture factory where he was the plant manager instead of taking my usual summer job washing cars at a local car dealership. He sold me on the idea by telling me that I would be done by 3:30 in the afternoon and have the rest of the day to myself. What I did not know was that I would be starting work every day at 7 a.m. When I left work, I was so tired I mostly went home and slept.

In order to drive home his "stay in school" message, my dad gave me one of the hardest jobs in the factory. I walked along a platform as wooden bookcases rolled by me on a conveyor belt. My job was to sand the top shelf. Never the middle shelf, only the top shelf! I did this eight hours a day, all summer long, and reached levels of boredom that I did not think were possible.

Lesson learned. After that job, I knew I wanted to stay in college and never have to work in a situation like that again. It also gave me a profound respect for people who work in grueling jobs such as that one in the furniture factory.

During high school, I played football and received a couple of scholarship offers to small colleges. However, my heart was set on going to college at the University of North Carolina at Chapel Hill. Once I arrived on campus, I found that I missed playing football. So, I walked onto the varsity football team and quickly found that college sports were more than I bargained for.

We practiced and lifted weights *all the time*. There was little chance to study and my grades began to suffer. Being good at football in high school did not translate to even being average at the college level. So, after one year, I made the decision to "walk off" of the football team and focus on getting into medical school.

Thankfully, a friend told me about the club football team at UNC. Club football is played in full pads and is kind of like JV football. We played all the local colleges, practiced infrequently, and were often known to have a beer after practice instead of Gatorade. It was the perfect activity for me and I ended up playing six years as they allowed me to stay on the team while I was in medical school.

My other rude awakening at college was how smart everyone was. I was surrounded by people who not only were in the top of their high school class, but were also from educated families and often grew up in big cities. I came from a small town and neither of my parents had a college degree. I remember vividly my first small discussion group when the girl across from me said, "We weren't allowed to go on the trip and I was *livid!*" I was totally smitten. Not only was she pretty but she also used "big" words that I had never heard before.

Being surrounded by this new "peer" group took some getting used to. Luckily, my roommate, Deckster, was my best friend from home. He had not traveled far from our small town of Lenoir much in his life, either. On our senior high school beach trip to Myrtle Beach, we were eating at a seafood buffet when we heard something crunching. We looked over and Deckster was eating the boiled shrimp without peeling them.

Once we explained how to eat them, he said, "I was wondering why people are always raving about shrimp. I thought they were disgusting."

It's not that we weren't as smart as other students at UNC, we just weren't very worldly. In a funny coincidence, one of the guys we hung out with from our dorm was even less worldly than we were. He was from a tiny town in the mountains of North Carolina. One morning at breakfast he exclaimed, "This is the hardest donut I have ever eaten!" It was a bagel.

The most important moment of my life occurred at UNC. I met my future soulmate. Ellen and I met during our sophomore years and have been together ever since. It is a cliche to describe your wife as your best friend, but for me it is absolutely true. God was definitely looking out for me when he brought her into my life. She always laughs at my jokes, even when they are not funny, and has been a wonderful mother to our children. After reading this book and learning about my personality, you will understand why everyone calls Ellen a saint.

I stayed in Chapel Hill and entered UNC medical school in 1992. Between the studying and the long hours of residency I basically missed the '90s. Trying to absorb all the information the professors throw at you has been likened to drinking out of a fire hydrant.

One of my lowest points was on a sunny Saturday afternoon. I was walking to the library to study and I had to walk through a large parking lot full of families tailgating before a UNC football game. The year before, I would have been with them but in medical school there are no days off.

Even though medical school was tough, I still found ways to have fun. During my first summer break, Ellen and I headed to the Outer Banks and found jobs in a seafood restaurant. Waiting tables was an entirely new learning experience and one I never quite mastered. The restaurant where we worked was small and we had to be bartenders as well as wait on tables.

Once, after making an entire table of six frozen daiquiris, I overheard someone say, "Susan, how are you enjoying your virgin daiquiri?"

I looked at the glass which was now half-full and asked, "Did you say VIRGIN?"

They were very understanding when I told them I had missed that very important word when she ordered. She was eighteen, and I know you have heard this one before, *but she looked much older.*

Ellen and I got married after my second year of medical school and we moved into a small house. During the third year of medical school, students are sent around the state for a month at a time to work in various clinics and hospitals. The accommodations during these rotations were usually pretty sparse but during one rotation I actually had to live in a funeral home! It was a bit creepy as I had to stay there at night by myself.

There was one night, however, that I did find my temporary "home" to be a lot of fun. On this particular night, they were having a viewing in the front of the building. Evidently, a small group of kids decided to explore a little. I heard them whispering and trying to open every door as they came down the hall. When they touched my doorknob,

I let out a loud, bloodcurdling scream and shook the door. This was followed by four equally loud screams as the kids ran down the hall.

I can feel you judging me. My grandmother used to say, "Laughter is good for your health" and I was not feeling very healthy that month.

During the last year of medical school, I had to decide what specialty to go into. I loved the idea of working with kids all day but my main fear was boredom. I tend to bore easily and I was afraid pediatrics would just be one runny nose after another.

Therefore, I decided I was going to be a family medicine doctor. As I did more adult rotations, however, I noticed that the more I took care of adult patients, the less I enjoyed medicine. I did not enjoy seeing one adult after another with health problems that were often caused by poor lifestyle choices. Not to mention that I felt powerless to influence these choices.

Everything became crystal clear to me one Friday afternoon at the end of my family practice rotation. I was taking a history from an overweight, diabetic, smoking male who was on thirteen different prescription medicines. He was becoming very grumpy with my thoroughness and finally said, "Can you hurry up? I am just here to get a refill of my pain meds."

I left that room feeling grumpy myself, but luckily this was about to change. In the very next room, I was seeing a cute little five-year-old boy who had strep throat. I looked at him and said, "You know where you got strep throat, don't you? From smooching with girls."

He looked shocked, and then replied, "I only kissed her on the cheek!"

That was a pivotal day in my journey to becoming a pediatrician. The contrast between the patient types was stark enough to make me realize which direction I wanted to take my career. I wanted to take care of children!

I have never regretted my decision and enjoy every day I spend with these small, unfiltered, and ever-developing human beings.

The other great thing about pediatrics is that it lets me live out my childhood dream of being a comedian, at least on a small scale. Every room I go into is an opportunity to tell a joke or share a funny story. Just like in the movie *Monsters University*, children's laughter is the fuel that keeps me going.

After medical school, I went on to do my pediatric residency at UNC hospitals. Many of my professors encouraged me to go somewhere like Boston or Chicago to finish my training but I loved living in Chapel Hill. I would have stayed there forever except our first child arrived during my third and final year of my training.

Both Ellen and I were raised in small towns and that culture meant something to us. We couldn't see raising a family in a bustling college town. So, even though I had a job offer at Chapel Hill Pediatrics, we headed for the country and settled in our forever home of Shelby.

Shelby, North Carolina, is a town of about 2,000 people. It's known as the "City of Pleasant Living." Our town is located at the confluence of the beautiful rolling foothills of the Blue Ridge Mountains and the bustling Metrolina region of the Carolinas. The quaint downtown is surrounded by farmland and scenic byways.

Shelby is similar in many ways to my hometown of Lenoir which is about forty miles to the north. When people ask me why we didn't move to Lenoir, the answer is simple. No one is going to trust their child to the "Brian" that they knew when I was growing up. In Shelby, I was "Dr. Benfield" from Chapel Hill and that brought with it a level of trust I would never be able to get in my hometown.

I joined the only pediatric group in Shelby known as the Shelby Children's Clinic. It was, and still is, staffed by a group of well-educated physicians and is highly thought of in medical circles. The main thing that attracted me to this practice was that the quality of medicine practiced at this clinic was far superior to the small-town clinics I saw patients from at UNC Hospitals during my training. When I joined, I was the sixth physician and the clinic has grown to include eleven doctors, three mid-level providers, a psychologist, and a nutritionist.

As you can tell from this book, I am incredibly happy with my choice to become a pediatrician and to join the Shelby Children's Clinic. I have met so many great families and have been privileged to have wonderful partners and a fantastic staff. If I had to do it over again, I would not change a thing (except maybe all those times I stuck my foot in my mouth!).

As I write this final chapter, I feel a great deal of relief to be finally done. It's been like having a term paper that is due, but for five years!

In a great coincidence, I was putting the finishing touches on the book when the song, "Dancing in the Dark" by Bruce Springsteen came on and I heard the lyric *I'm sick of sitting 'round here trying to write this book.*

I gave a mental nod to Bruce and thought I could not have said it better!

The artwork for this book has been done by a talented young artist named Cooper Bridges. Cooper, who is now in high school, has been my patient since birth. When she was eleven, she drew a picture of me and gave it to me during one of our visits. I knew then that I wanted her to create all the art in this book.

I would like to thank you for reading my stories and helping me become a world-famous author. Okay, just an author, but that is still more than my first-grade teacher ever thought I would accomplish!

Thank you also to all my patients and their parents who make me laugh and make my job so much more enjoyable.

And to "yogurt boy," thank you for the inspiration to put these stories on paper for others to hear. Who would have thought that a child's fear that he was going to have to cover his private parts with a certain dairy product could inspire someone who is very averse to writing to write an entire book.

ABOUT THE AUTHOR

Brian Benfield was born and raised in Lenoir, North Carolina. He attended the University of North Carolina at Chapel Hill, where he received both his undergraduate and medical degrees. After completing his pediatric training in 1999, Dr. Benfield joined the Shelby Children's Clinic. He is married, with one son and two daughters, and has lived on a farm in his home state since 2004. He still does not know what he wants to be when he grows up.

Made in the USA
Columbia, SC
16 April 2024

34466866R10150